„Let me not to the marriage of tru

impadivence. Love is not which alte. _ ... _

autorotation finds or bends with the remover.

ever fixed mark that looks on tempest,

never shaken, the star to every wondering bark.

Whose worth unknown although its height would be

taken. Love is not time's fool, though rosy lips and

cheeks, within his bending sicco' s compest cup.

Love alters not with his breif hours and weeks but

bares it out, even to the edge of dune, if this we

error and upon me proved.

I never rid no no man ever loved."

- Patrick Stewart -

Imprint

The present text has been edited with the utmost care. The publication is protected by copyright. All rights lie with the author. No part of the book may be written without permission of the publisher in any form by photocopy, film or other processes are reproduced. Also the rights of reproduction by lecture, radio and TV is reserved. The German National Library lists this publication in the Deutsche Nationalbibliografie.

© 2020 Heike Thieme, Production and publishing:
BoD - Books on Demand, ISBN 978-3-7519-1568-7

« Heike Thieme »

5

Wild horses shouldn't be tamed. The heart is loved but is a Wildflower.
From eating less meat to walking at work.
Earth is a blessed be, like the one we love. Love her, but leave her wild.

Politicians should think.
Thinking should solve problems.
And through their actions, they should influence the decisions.
So you should go to your politician,
and say what you want,
then he has to represent that for you,
it will be a movement that we all like
for the community.
Power comes from the people.
But when the people are silent and mob,
then what should change outside ?

Give me the time to get wiser, sothen I ll understand what is your meaning,
what things you are looking, what you have in remember words telling to
my heart, once a day we spendt time together, another day we ll continue.
We are travelling in two boats now, but we are the same crew. I Love You.

Isn't it charming to see the crows in black dance, reflected again the
misteroius sky ? I think really, your Dog is very beautiful and has a
knowledge in her sight. I'm so happy she is with you they do speak
thelepatically but it's up to us, to understand.

THE GATHERING OF CROWS
ONE CROW FOR SORROW,
TWO CROWS FOR JOY,
THREE CROWS FOR A GIRL,
FOUR FOR A BOY,
FIVE CROWS FOR SILVER,
SIX CROWS FOR GOLD,
SEVEN CROWS FOR A SECRET NEVER
TO BE TOLD

Neighborhood initiatives are changing the situation
in a district organization, the solidarity network
doesn't leave people alone.
The situation will no longer be perfect for anyone.
We are all people in a global family.
What applies to the individual also applies to everyone !

Will he still have work tomorrow or not ?
Will a part-time worker be sent straight to the social welfare office ?
Do old people have to go to the gym to withstand the strain
and still be able to work ?
Will grasshoppers exploit all workplaces ?
Is it really that difficult to get back into jobs ?
Why are half of all insecure jobs done by women ?
Those in need wear old clothes and can't afford the dentist,
and ongoing bills are cause for concern.
If the state cuts all the benefits of the poor,
The precariat lets live on the edge of debt.
Whoever does not work like an ox is dropped.
We come from all walks of life and backgrounds.
We should be proud of ourselves together and enjoy celebrating.
If the working conditions are bad, it affects everyone as well.

Dirndl wearers always look like melancholy transvestites.
If women were not to become doctors,
as a nurse they would have to limit themselves financially considerably.
I will not become a soldier, because women have to be too embarrassing in
politics alone, so not with a gun in my hand !
Or should women in the judiciary just find a system
that shows her undressed ?
If, unfortunately, nuns themselves are for free up and down priests sexually ,
such an old profession is no longer popular.

That's very right, unfortunately nowadays things have changed considerably in the field of job and in general every day consideration for every living being. The age of work is growing and even the elder people are forced to work even if they hadn't any strongs to go on. But, reality is reality and we shall keep healthy and trying to reinvent our work all the time.

Yes upstairs We Women are responsible for the most deaths, but downstairs most time the Men are responsible for this.... hihi

Ain't it the truth !

It's not a good idea, friends.
Would we have to worry ?
How do the Democrats in the USA want to move in the future ?
Does democracy still have room to breathe there ?
Who flies too high approaches the earth very quickly.
The rest of the world has already proven that to us.
But let's wait and see how all of your adventurers like to say.
Let us dare to adventure ... HaHaHaHa !!!!
Choose a despot …

Calm I m still here. Who ever tried to divide us, would fall back to himself, like a Baby Doll, that never learned to think mature, never talked wise. They can't copy what German Nazis managed long before. You have Your own culture in North America ! How could a camel and a bagder build one circle ? And if those stupid thinking young slow learning idiots in your country decide to continue that way, they ll have to learn about their history like everybody does.

You are the experienced part of your nature and culture. You might teach them, when time has come.

Good to Do and enjoy your peaceful time and start into anew Day as Good
as he comes ! Of course. Some organize, they won't get any Babies anymore
in England. Some won't work digitally for no social payment in Spain
anymore. Some will be out of stand to choose any kind of professions like
the Bible told us Women to do in Germany. Some won't stand behind
politics that work against optimism in our folk in Skandinavia. Some hold
on to fall in love in Russia. Some would just marry as Women with a
Woman in Ukraine. Some work it out without being in their Motherly
Womb a whole life through and open up their mouths in every village !

Yes, of course I would have better my child
should give birth on the island of "Föhr",
it is said that there is not much stolen there.
Then maybe I wouldn't have the child
stolen from the puerperium,
just because a few scrapped junkies denounced it.
Of course, I could have asked forgiveness on all fours,
then I would have been offered an assistant position for comfort,
limited of course, with the only exception,
if I let myself be made pregnant again by anybody, who cared who it was,
to be considered a birthing machine and possibly one day
maybe I got a job at church, acting like those,
who rigorously goes against all forms of anti-social abuse.
But to do that I would have to join the Church
and offer a few more children to official state abuse.
Who else would come along like that and would be an honest woman,
who has nothing to ask about work than me ?

When I read those own words I sometimes could eat a whole cow not to
freak out ! I said Cow not Crow ! I was never never able to eat that kind of
Bird that saved my life running away !!

I will Love You My Sweet Beautiful Flower.
We will Be In The wild Full Of Nature.

I know to prefer the evenings when I would listen to seldom words, and wait until I see the Crow going to sleep.

We are in the middle fields with our horses and we sit on our picnic blanket.

Take care, might be that you had not soo much luck with me, when I would follow my past, I had nothing to say, and when I have nothing to say, there is no way in falling in love. I might be honest. But I think I was not able to shut up my thoughts. I might not able to survive in my soul in forgettin about all.

I was altime warned about the consequences as a Woman in my german culture, and that warning came from an old lady who was a survivor of "Ausschwitz" an old jewish lady, but today I knew what's all about that, from my past until today, from her sufferings and mine and my son's, so todays system that was build on these gruel fantasies and a degenerated way of thinking.

I really hardly hope that You made me believe one day in something that lets me thinking of "Living and Let be Alive" !

It is so good to have real friends more, sothat I could have started to let things flow. I was nearly at the point to brake, because a big past can pull you under, if this is never said.

My flower I will always be at your side, when you feel in a way I can make my words heal and comfort you, you are my heart and I love you.

Im eating My Mozzerella sticks and Your welcome.

Never try to look back to that awful monster was for too many Women and Kids and Men, old and young, pregnant and sisters and brothers, Artists, Musicians, Actors, Writers, Magicians, whole generations, villages full of people, all dead.

I am so happy for U not to have lived all these years in our "culture" and none would have broken your heart.

There are reasons for U to be happy to be !
Brrrrrrrrrrrrrrrrrrrrr !
I was baking small rolls today. I am full.

You must be cold my flower sending warmth to you.

Indeed. I remember you did this several times.
I imagine them all who miss such solidarity.

I will do it many of times.

This gives hope.

Tell me if you have problems, do you have a sibling or friend who could help you out ? It could be a reason that they change to 5G, they already told me to not to wonder, because sometimes in the start, the old devices don't start as usual.

We have much better skills even being ladies. What is reality is that truth lies behind society, not everyone is accepted as they teach us, it is not true, not everyone is equal. Cause females in the eyes of many companies are still considered lower than men, just because they fear that female might have children, and might need more time off.

I remember that I altime loved to be with and to work with the handicapped. So I searched for talks to other intelligent women, and for good friends to my son. But we both were excluded because of this !
To be solidary to people they are afraid off ! To be friends with darksinned people all around. To accept other women's kids, they were alone educated. To tolerate the elderly and learn from all this, and teach us kids respect. To educate in the meaning of integrate all sicknesses and fears and

philosophic different meanings. To let our sons talk sameway like those
better daughters from better houses. To let our kids decide what to believe
and when. To choose their mighty father they love, without press from
motherhood. To speak and to laugh out loud, when things lie on their soul
and asholes around come out.

In these remarks there is an observation of social stupidity that is still
archaic. I suspect that the man who has not been a powerful hunter for a
long time may be afraid of losing his supremacy, and therefore weakness
hinders human progress. Nothing on earth that a man cannot do, a woman
cannot do. We develop in confusion and must not lose our judgment.
Thank you to those who share their feelings with me.
I draw this picture, which for me symbolizes the transition from the past to
the future. It is a very optimistic feeling.

Time has come when everything has to change !

However - whatever - whenever - don't feel under pressure - I know how
stressy that work with handicapped can be - You do what You want -
and this is fine ! You are still young, there is so much to understand before
resting and getting old, there is time to change more thoughts and find
election even once Your gettin old.

Virus in China.
Forest fires in Australia.
Earthquake in Turkey.
Volcanic eruptions in the Philippines.
So politicians state that they are only concerned with the good of the earth,
and tell, how does the earth thank us now ?
It is no longer all about our earth.
Climate change is imminent.
Mother Earth is going through the menopause.
Sometimes she is a bit irritable.
She gets hot flashes.

Moist areas dry out. Others are starting to flood.
The poles - breasts - are no longer so tight.
There are dents and holes in the sky of orange skin in the ozone layer.
Earth used to have changeable moods only in April,
now she spins all year round.
And what does a person ask - is our best time already over ?
And the Mitlife crisis shows that he falls head over heels in love
with a sixteen-year-old who tells the world -
How dare you, such an environmental swine! -
Yes, she is the little darling of all old politicians ....
Nature is not a mother. She is a choleric madman who has been hitting us
for millennia and who, let's be honest, doesn't love us deep down at all !
Mother Earth doesn't love humans.
Better people now learn the truth,
before some may die of a flu virus.
And they're not always friendly,
who hide behind kindness !
It points to the metaphor of women as fertile ground.
Gaia (earth) is an uncontrollable force among the Greeks.

It is very likely that the break between earth and man has already
progressed. The lack of understanding of the symbiotic system that animates
life forms pushes us aside and naturally leads to our own destruction. The
most serious problem is that we harm other living species and drag
ourselves into our restlessness and stupidity.
It is strange that I have the feeling that this sad imbalance has occurred in
the old days when man did not yet exist. The positive thing about this
process is that every earthly will, alien to human thought, is responsible for
restoring a balance, the idea of balance of which is completely elusive,
because this will has projects that go far beyond human intelligence.

I like this quote from de Lautréamont (Isidore Ducasse 1846-1870)

"The bright past has made great promises for the future; it will keep them"

"Our lives begin to end the day we become silent about things that matter."
-Martin Luther King Jr.

Needs another constitution to make democracy possible. Today I ask who wanted democracy ? Power-obsessed old white sacks coming from the few schools for privileged whites. Schools where the truth is not taught .They divide, rush and oppress people in a country that will never belong to them. They never have been great hunters and cling to all the rest of their power. The idiots march to war for them, and do rob and pillage, drink and rape for them. With poverty is allowed every unfair game. Immigrants and Mexicans have to stay outside. Climate is already striking back and it is already seeping through that they will never defeat nature. Americans will remember this time to answer for and consider what white man destroyed and how much suffering he caused.
Where ever those hands came to keep us alive, like all of us know, there was one who suffered exactly the same under force and pressure.
Wherever our fate took us to make a new start.
We all knew, every kind of knowledge was experience of others before.

In fact I am not perfect - but I don't work on it too !

Do You See us Like Me ? Sometimes its like the Sun I be, and You the Moon instead, and just that pond water between. I think We Both might have been twins life ago. Could that have been both in Mothers Womb prepared to feel the same.

Women's secret is always coming out a cave.

Your about To Tell in a whole Book.

See my Boobs, they are two. See my Eyes them both. See my hands, and feet and knees, all two. See us both in mother 's breathe inside. She laughs and we breathe.

The whole world will Know our true Love. They will Know what real Love and Kindness Is.

It fades away and Comes Reborn. Each Time There is somthing New.
A New Story a New Energy a new share.

This is quiet easy said.

We can see it in the eyes of young people, they might have been old parents, in another time, another life. Everybody could have been this.

Sun and Moon.

All these thousands of years we came and went and all of them were family once, even some are out there deciding to come back when time has come.

Should not happen, that Sun and Moon get too close, sothat we stop to turn, and maybe we rock together and burst with it. Then Sun would come close, too. And wupps she might eat us up or we both would fall right into the heat of the Sun. Until she would burst to a monster. And we would see Sun explode and dissapear to a small magnetic hole that catches everything, and all planets around would follow this.

That is indeed the chaos.

But how I see, that is the imagination of a Child, that looks back to a family of irrational people they find no hold in reality. I am just coming from there. But my lifetime is longer than only this one time. I look back to them, I seem to feel, that they be surrounded by rocks and see, that was not the answer of survival. And none would have taken them by their hands to explain them, what natural symbiose means.

To comfort each other we do need, to bear this world, to hold the burden, and watch them, like the fools running in their One-Way-Street.

Indeed.

You know, what I appreciate about you is that you are firstly a handsome man and secondly that you are absolutely loyal, and don't need to make me sure, since You are looking in my eyes, I really can See.

What are You gonna eat ? I had one real cuddle muddle, but it tasted good. I took a baking dish and put all things in like noodles, eggplant, hack, tomato juice, and above cheese. Such a big thing I don't do very often.

Im eating hamburgers and I bought some beer and I bought some bread.

Yes, this week I didn't have normal bread, because I still have some selfmade rolls back.

Your making me hungry again.

Yes, I wished since days to make big walks with doggy, and we have one of the biggest storms in Germany. Each time we were outside, we came lucky dry home. But inside I saw the ice hamring against the window, even thunderstorm and icy rain. But I really wanted to walk around again. Then I might not eat too much. And Mable makes me thinking of her health. She has very big pauses for being in heat. I don't hope she is seriously sick. So we wait one two weeks more, then we go to a doctor.

Blessings to Mable sending her wellness and a hug.

But like the moment she is in a very good shape. She eats good. She is funny. She runs and has fun. The other dogs are smelling her beautiful flowersmell. But we still wait for her bleeding. Let me hope she is really fine. Such a surgery could be a financial catastrophe !

I like to stay calm and optimistic, so then everything will be fine. Our kitten

once had to die with such a problem, but for a long time we had to buy her special and expensive food. And before that we had those cute mice, my sun and me. But they do really have no very long life. It is too much for heart like mine, to cry because of a little mouse dying.
Yes, I believe the Good-Bye to each little furanimal is the worst.

My dear, how is Your tiny little Hiney right between Your legs there going, is he doing fine ?

Yes haha.

Oh fine. You sitting there enjoying food, and him asleep I bet.

Yes its sleeping.

How cute. Let him rest a while.
let him in his dream of little honey wet grasslands between my legs, and he will sure awake once and think we were inbetween.
Grows.

Yes, really ?

Good that THOSE little tiny furanimals don't shout out loud, when they awake !

Indeed.

Oh fuck, I just imaginated it they would do .... my Gosh !
Excuse my word .... I meant sorry.
No, now don't get angry ! It's Your BIRTHDAY !!! What can i say ...

I am angry about how good they are and then they are friends come in and say who is fake or real. So I said many words that will anger them. But they do not want to cross this wolf in a war !

Calm me withyour words.

I always calm by the thought, they are real greenhorns, because they still do know, what is up and down, or they devide the left and right, then notice the black and white, or just distinguish the Siro to the One. But in real there are no life experiences they would make them rich. I say, a real Man's life is as big as his challenges he showed and managed just to stay alive, all those Survival struggles that he fought, and at last the evidence he shows among friends ! That makes his charme, and not the financial carrier !

Who I am talking about these witches you know Im starting to think.

I don't want to spend time on this.

Ok I ll calm myself. Im smiling now.
Sorry. Sorry.

Okay. It's winter, we are inside, we have reasons to be happy.
Why not try to share positive thoughts ? There is snow outside.
We keep warm here. Winter gives us a feel of resting.
So why not build a bridge to other people ?

I ll try.

I see You are in trouble answering to this. But I clearly see, that I won't be me, who opens Your heart. You should do it on Your own. I ll never fight for this. I know everybody is his own teacher. Maybe You like it to see yourself in trouble. But then I can't help, because it is the way that You choose.

I love You. Lets just say they crossed my line and Im happy now.

Then it is going better now.

Yes I have you in my thoughts and I hear your words and i fell you kiss me and your saying it will be ok.

No, sorry, this might be hard. It won't be me for sure saying, it will be ok. Nevermind. I see You are the same Human like everybody is hurting. So now to explain it clear, it will be from now on too myself who hurts. I am like a human You be same like others, and we are no Angels, and Fairies, and Godesses any more, I hope You understand.

Really I will not give because of them.
They made me stronger with their words,
and yes I do hurt all the time.

Stop the wheels.

If You like to spend Your time with other witches, lightnings, thunder and fairy people, then there is no time for me, who is a real human and a woman, so realize to hold the contact to me, inholds to take steps into my direction with real interest, with tried respect, and not with holding back in any longings to other peoples magick, making you so strong. If You wanna keep One first and real friend in Me, You must prove that You are ready for reality, so You must share Your real thoughts and speak the truth, or I ll let You in Your visions and addiction to chaotic running with your wolfish loneliness. So Think of it. You have to decide maybe one Day !

I understand my flower. But magick is only what comes to me.
I love You infinity.

Sometimes You play tricks, and I am not made for this.

I do love you my flower that is not a trick.

Then I start to imagine You sittin there maybe for a long time alone on the chair at a long bar table and watch your lonely whiskey drink very alone ...

And I am listening. I am always alone thinking of you showing up through that door in the bar, and taking my hand and walking me out.

Babe your awful. I know You have still daylight.

I am speaking my truth my love really.

Yes, and tomorrow someone is passing and telling me, that he saw an UFO. Then next one comes along and said he wonders why he understood Jesus is living by him, and he was chosen.

I say that because You are turning all the same wheel for whole lifetime. You would never see behind Your walls. All those beings outside the wall have their own views. Nothing is important. I do have my realtiy. You have Yours. And between both of us there is the third reality, that none of us will ever know ! Why You always think, that only Yours is the most important ? I don't. I go now. I love you infinity.

No Nature will answer You. But it is just You decides to shut you up.

Your making me laugh.

You do the same.

I do choose you now. Show me the way then.

No way.

Why are You being so then ?

I am proved in longing through a long cold winter.

All I did was speak my truth and this believe me.
I think about you all the time.

I am sorry to hear that one person is not who she made herself out to be. Unfortunately, that happens all to often in Your country like people tell. I start to realize what is meant with Political Correctness. Each time one abuses to get intelligent answers. Tell about their friends, or direct speech about equality, and the chances for everybody, then always express her soaking wet, deepest regret, but encased in hypocritical pity that is without any depth. I am not really proud that I made to know her, because it was just her foolish noisy "Hello my best friend and Sister and Teacher and Writer". She ain't really on my wavy line, because her real side is another. It seems reprehensible to me to shove all people over the crest like this, and to have true pity, but to want to know nothing about their background, even to describe this as too pathological and too superfluous or far too complicated. That is my opinion, and it describes the normal racist behavior, I say.
And now I don't wonder why unexperienced people climb into your life, be such good friends, and from one second to another, when you have told enough, you realize them telling the other worse things about you. There is no chance. They brake with everybody and fuck around like pigs fresh from the meatfarm with a license to be privilegued. How do they dare to be superficial just to hurt the other and find it good ?
There is my loneliness in Germany the better one.
I never had it like this.

This is what I told to Carrie also, and this is a thing unfortunately, that happens all to often for her liking. That is one reason she isolates herself, same to me and same to You. I will not talk to Tracey again, I promise.

HAPPY BIRTHDAY !
Just, my Frank, have a nice Day, this are people telling that are sober and clean in the head, You can be sure that I exactly choose from these to be the real friend, who is not too talkactive and a liar. Just a few people but the right ones.

Hej Frank - Are You Out There ?

Yes.

I have done one mistake.
Let me tell You .... I wondered why my blog doesn't work. I waited and
waited for my second blog, then today I searched the old blog, and it was
deleted. Then I finally checked my text I send to them again. And I saw the
damage that was done. Because of them telling me to be so tolerant to
publish each of my thoughts and I really could talk free what I wanted, so I
talked a bit critical about the way of political behaviour, some might think
about the consequences, and I said right away, that we Germans too didn't
own the privilege to be "Golden Hearts" with a heart „Full of Love", our
history we have to answer to, things been done, since we had that privilege
back to be mature people. They took away my name as author and the first
blog, too. I was so sad.
Then I wrote a mail to apologize a bit - I wrote -
„I have chosen last days to find myself. But what I learned is, that You
promote real Art. I should deliver my creativity, so I ll go ahead. This Art
portal would publish me more, if I painted more good Paint Art. So I must
not hang around in sadness. I should paint. I m sure You will contact me
again. It depends on what's my offer and creativity. It always helps to create.
Just some tryings I want to show, just have a look and see. Then tell me,
when it's time, that I do the right thing. I hope my answer works."

awww My Flower Im sorry. I Hope so too.

I showed him some nice paintings. And tomorrow I ll come back to paint
some of a bit again. It won't be that easy. Hopefully Xavi will answer me.

Here's a virtual hug my Love. I like your paintings indeed.

I wrote these words again explain more to the fact,
that this what I did was against all Art...

How was Your day ?

My Day was Good.

That woman is noisy again ... what shall I do ? I just ignore her.
If there was that botton to escape our talk for ever. I did.
This i called mute. She doesn't know that I don't read hers anymore.

Like You had that problem with such a witch and finally you blocked her.
She wants to start talks about me, and talk about everything she knows
about me, to others who miss it to get in touch with me, not to be lonely
anymore. She is bad. I see it is necessary. I should learn next time, not to
trust in any younger american ladies who want to know all but just to put
themselves in a better shape, pretending to be one they just wanted to be.
Now I block her.

Ufff Now my day was good too.

Im Glad my flower. Now you see what I mean.

Yes, I bet she is a maniac, that could never learn from the wisdom I gave her. And like Carrie said, this happened often to her. Sothat I might think, that all these prettiest stories they file out for everybody are just the try not to be bored, and to have for each one they find as mature his very own parallels of life, to make themselves interesting.

Indeed.

This seems really poor minded. I bet she is at work pretty outsider and missunderstood in her young age, and abuses people to make them depend on her speech, because at work she is bored and incompetend enough, like all young women who have no adventures or such a boredom with a husband who has no opinion or bravety to say "No". She must have aggressions because of all that, and she is ashamed that her parents don't even trust her, and never talked openly to her, and her father votes republican. I think it is her who has the bigger trouble if I say so.

MY DEAR ! What I learned about the work with the handicapped but like we said Mature Handicapped people, was the very first principe not to talk about them to the outside. And Tracey is a scatterer about everybodies private things, so her handicapped, and she puts all that stoff in the only one pottery, and finally she thought everybody else without her was handicapped in a way, that she would have to therapy like an anmateur. But at last we do laugh about this, because she is still learning. And she will do so many faults, until one will pass her aside and tell her to shut up her mouth and go home better and not to desturb the "handicapped" with her stupid speech ! That is real happening too, if she provokes more, and she won't lean on others she is cheeting on them.

Do You like to talk more ?
This is Your DAY don't let You get upset of this things.

Im making Dinner and Im just relaxing my love.

You want these ones and more .... ?

Sure.

And those ?

They search for Art and nothing else .... I must do it.

They are not really like I am on the search for my words ....

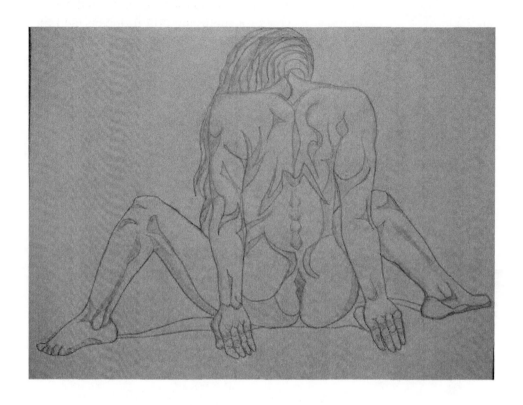

I ll collect my strength and finally go ahead !

Artist that stays passively is no Artist ... and resignating is like undone work is unforgiving myself...

29

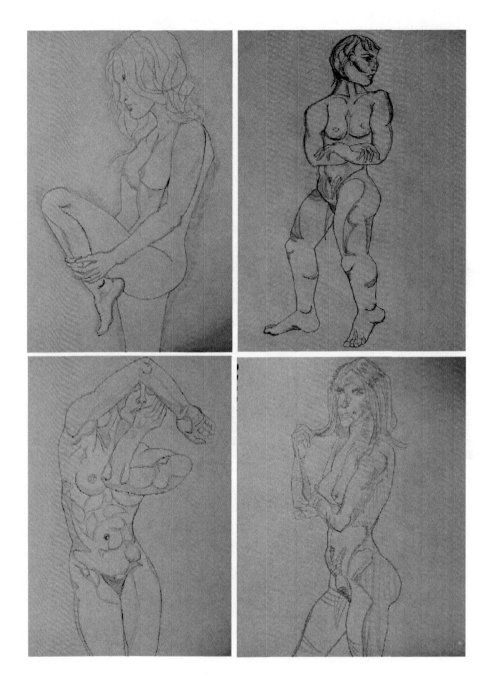

30

You draw so well.

I kiss Your Budy.

I have that feeling, that prickles in my veins. My fantasy. My vulcany.

Yes, now You know it is what I would like to share with U.

But we ll never do.

Upps. But we sit here together under a night sky with the fullmoon, and have our warm socks, and do dream of it.

Indeed.

This is a Good Birthday, this is the proof that You never do age, because a never ending Birthday is an everlasting Birth without a brake !!

Indeed my flower gonna go eat now sleep well.

Til then.

Whoever is careless with the truth in small matters
cannot be trusted with important matters. — Albert Einstein

I hear them signals from outer space. I am wondering who tells them. Same lights and flickers from inside of my blood. And exploding to my Love that I bear. From my deepest sickering, climbing up to my Mood. I came from the sea riding the wave and carried by the wind to reach that coast. The balance in between every drop of water jumping me up the fields and fall down the rocks, running through the stone and spread into the sea. Can't hide and close my eyes knowing where ever I ll be. In your Arms that I ll be.

I am The Shadow. Unseen Howls of The Lycan Whispers Circle You.

"I used to think he was the strangest person in the world, but then I thought: There are so many people in the world, there has to be someone like me who has been harmed as much as I feel." - Frida Kahlo

It is a good sign and real solidarity being in mind with People you won't just have to assume that you imagine things and dream of them.

So I let my Women and Friends tell about Life, and summarize. Who knew about me so far away ? Who wanted to know about me ? I see how many things are able to do and survive, and give them hope ! Especially could it be a life help for younger people, who need a direction.

Yes !!

I just see because what I did in just seven Years - I published 57 books and painted for an exhibition online. And how many wonders I saw with this, and processed in my mind, and produced in fantasy, and evolved a healing, developed a good friend to everybody, that shares with me !

That is just a Life Power that You bring, and it needed all my time to find a way out, like a lion in my chest, and now he does talk and roar like a king !

But I must be modesty, because within that big number of books, are 22 translated in English by me. But this was too a product of creativity to enfold with each creation a kind of light in the sky. Those souls they walk and pass by will wonder.

Yes they will !

But I will have to produce, and work out more, now I am responsible for this. Ok. I better now go off, not to get weird of all that stoff, my Godness !

That was so funny. We were on our way back from the small woods, when a nice old couple passed. Forest rangers have just cut down many beautiful large trees. The trails are muddy and wet. And my dog looked like a wood piglet. But people said something so funny. They said they walk a lot and a lot, they've just been walking through the city for three hours, on the banks of the Schlei and out into the forest, and they are about three kilometers to go to pick up their car ... Hahahaha. These are people who prefer to walk and only think at the very end that they shouldn't leave their car alone for so long. I get the moths ! Hahahaha.

To be lonely makes you sad and lonely. I know it is not easy that Lover thing with hot and cold and togetherness and loneliness, and give and take and come and go. I might fall to deep in Love, and could not come back on earth. Then I might miss him so much and loose myself mourning. Then he might be not in the mood to talk, and I would nearly explode feeling missunderstood. Then he is a Man. And I am different to him. And altime me doing all my best, and him hide away. And me giving up all my Art and him thinks it is normal.

I can't go back to where it all began. So I would say, in this short life I am not made for relationship and living in the same place with someone. I am much too sensitive or reasonable for this.

That english word 'sensible' sounds like the german word 'sensibel' - but your word means that something 'makes sense' - but the german says 'sensibel' is same like 'sensitive'.

So now I say it right - That I altime must be reasonable, because for me partnership makes no sense since I met no one to love.

Yes, you can't have everything in life, but I really come from grandparents they loved all Art, Nature and Music. So they all loved independance. So I do realize, why these or that things do matter in my life.

A chancellor leaves. She had never really got into politics.
New elections for lobbyists. Election slogan - "I can't, but I would."
"I can become something on Will's talk show." "I - I - I"
She said "I can - I want and I will !"became"I could - I wanted but I won't !"
She would have preferred to spend a day in the 3rd sex toilet rather than
worrying about her party's mistakes at that time. Even she, as party leader,
was not even let in by the party and had to wait for admission because she is
no longer respected. Who will sign up for the party fart and new chair in the
future ? If it is the case that young brats, better daughters from a good
family, simply for doing an internship, and simply taking care cases in a
wheelchair outside for a walk, are described as "competent", people from
lower or middle classes know how our country is doing. There is no
professional knowledge, experience and intuitive approach that is required,
but privilege !

This knocks out the bottom of the barrel.

It is that disabled people here in Germany have been declared dead because they are so economical. If you do not agree, you will no longer get a job !

Breathe, Breath in the air. Don't be afraid to care. Leave, don't leave me. Look around, Choose your own ground. Long you live and high you fly. Smiles you'll give and tears you'll cry. And all you touch and all you see. Is all your life will ever be. Breathe. - Pink Floyd

Hi, Carrie !

Just in that second I gave my book - Directions to Future Days - to the publisher. It was real fun to produce this One ! I hope You enjoy it, too ! In all the hurry I didn't keep the cover to show You now, this meant we have to wait until Wednesday I think to recieve it, and see it online. Thanks for Your blessings, my Dear, and Good Day to Your Valentine's Day to You And Bob ! Carrie - my Godess ! Let me tell You my News ! I got the answer from The3NinesArts from Xavi Daniel .... He said the technical problem will be done now, the restruction of lost Blogs will be shown within the next two months, so my ones, too. And he invited me to get involved into his internal team, and they wanted me to be with, and soon he will explain this all to me !! With the Team !!
And this is the best I ever heard for the whole Year ! Tomorrow I ll paint again.

I ll be active, and these are the steps I ll do, and to use the energy to get power myself. The old story altime just allowed me to be a sacrifice for others.Them only spread there wings, these moments when I was really in my deepest mood and couldn't stand up anymore. But I am no more howling with the moon and wait for next sadness, that everybodies very true right to do things to make themselves feel better and share with people in a social system better than in isolation and stagnation.

This world of Art is a very huge how I can see !

You was with Frank the first Friends of so far away, that noticed, that I was worth it, too. And now I do manage to contact the world to transform all this big Idea to every country in the world, sharing universal Love !

My talk to Xavi Daniel -

I have chosen last days to find myself.
But what I learned is, that You promote real Art.
I should deliver my creativity, so I ll go ahead.
This Art portal would publish me more, if I painted more good Paint Art.
So I must not hang around in sadness. I should paint.
I m sure You will contact me again. It depends on what's my offer and creativity. It always helps to create.
Just some tryings I want to show, just have a look and see.
Then tell me, when it's time, that I do the right thing.

Blessings, Heike

I would not repeat that again, what definitely goes against all Art. But I was thinking the whole last two weeks like a robot, and published in ten days exact three books. But I missed too the time to paint and calm down again, what I have managed now. Give me one more chance, and I will do my best.

Like I wrote You, I could see that my Words inbetween political advices or mistreating people had not the best style. I ll use this second chance to concentrate more on the Art and not to use the word as political weapon.
I am not politician. I wanna be fair and present what I can.
You can choose the ones you want for Your creation.
Just that I didn't make You feel irritated.

Many greetings, Heike

Hi Heike I go on a trip for two months. At this time we will be reinstating the articles that were published and fell from the web. Also, from March to mid-April we will just readjust the art project. On my return I will call you, I would like you to get involved on the web at the level of being part of the internal team, I will explain. See you soon. A hug Xavier Daniel !

Yep …. a bit.

I can't understand my Aunt, why she said to be lonely so many years and she didn't try to find friends, or try for example visiting the elderly in their homes, or do some sport in the gym and get close to her neighbors ? She would never do. But why she chose that lonely life then, with the only contacts she uses in each days phonecalls to the whole world.
But this is altime the same question, why do people things and why they don't. There ain't no answer, and I see, sameway they ll altime have troubles understand an artist, so I will not be able to understand, why people don't search for social contacts ?

It is all very easy to understand, they way You live in your own balance and own selflove, makes you know, you are never alone, that is what each handicapped in his wheelchair tells me with his sympathy and smile in the eyes ! These are the people who are worth it !!

Friends, You see this includes or both ups and downs. We both are shocked about a world. But be are able to understand so much. Then within those pauses, when we relax, trust, fall and dive immediately happens the opposite, that things might reach us and come up, who feel hurting much. Because Life isn't a dream. Then we like all the others must carry our pack, we must learn to differenciate people, see those different characters and listen to them who tell about it. Sothen we feel strength and that makes us feel sober.

But we need to let us live in peace.

Stay like this. I have a vow not to let someone fall.

Good evening Heike, It happens that a certain number of human beings understand the same things, especially the increased sensitivity, makes it possible to feel the disturbing elements which are diffused on the whole of the planet by a minority of individuals, and which unfortunately are followed by too much the terrestrial citizens who do not take into account their sensitivity which could be considered weak, which is a big mistake. The principles of competitiveness worry us from wrong angles, because these principles have no happy endings in the medium or long term for the greatest number and worse still, the contempt for the substrate that carries us. I join you in the need to identify positive beings who develop real and benevolent collective actions. Force is energy, so we must try to direct it towards beings and projects that have a vision in time.

I like this quote from Thomas Hardy: "It is difficult for a woman to define her feelings in a language mainly used by men to express theirs."
I wish you a pleasant and peaceful weekend.

Long is my way, short is my life, feel young in heart
but as a lonely wolf I know a long and hard way,
as mother I feel free, as woman I m on my way !

Carrie my Blessings from Heike !

Good Morning! I woke early and didn't stay up for very long. I am tired today. I feel the weight of the world and it is too heavy to carry now. I will try to sleep some more and see if I can wake up later and feel lighter. My Bob got home sometime overnight as I lay sleeping. I hope he enjoyed the supper and coffee I had waiting for him ! He now rests in dreamland beside me as I lay back in bed. Too sore, myself to get up now. The Winter cold is hard on my dilapidated body so I slowly nurse myself back to a functioning level. Luckily our dog Missy will have gone out when Bob got home so it gives me a few extra hours this morning to rejoin the human race !

Face with tears of joy ! Morning is always harder, especially this time of year as the stiffness sets into my muscles and bones while I sleep. Really resting is always just out of arms' reach as the Arthritis and Fibromyalgia broil just beneath the surface of my skin. So I live in a state of out-of-body experience.

The only way to deal until Summer arrives as Spring is cold and wet here as well. The Indians, my Ancestors believed that a person with symptoms like mine was in touch with the Spirit Realms in constant state of one foot in each place. I have always felt this !

Yes today I definitely have one foot in each world, different realities... I feel my family that have gone on before me So intensely in the early morning as they visit me. Checking to see how I am doing and teaching me a new resilience of spirit and body. Giving me the strength to face another day in this body and tortured world of blind people who, all too often, are driven by hatred, greed and intense fear. Their mind-numbing fear depletes my spirit and I am grateful each day when my family come to refresh my soul. We must (humankind) have these oasis-like moments of reprieve and repose. When all the world sleeps. I truly make the most of them.

Have a blessed day ! Dearest Sister, your friendship means another means of refreshment for my Spirit! Health, happiness and blessings dear one !

I do love You so, too.

Love you Sister xxx

See those Giraffes in Masaai Reserve. I see'm in that world You describe between Spirit and Earth. A brave Heart like You living with a vulcany heat under skin and still walking along like them wandering on the Edge.
It hurts knowing about your pain.

Funny I adore Giraffes. I can relate to them !

This is unbelievable beautiful.

We are one !

On saturdays we both go the market usually. There we meet them we miss the whole week and they do miss us both. My sweet Mable gets Love, Attention, Smelling, Sausages as much as she wants. These people are not shy to tell that this dog is sensible for others feelings and they adore how she feels into others. She touches people so directly, carefully, soft, smelling loving their trousers, pushing with love and watching like a lady we can see, she once was a Kitten walking on Socks cuddling with everybody and especially Kids right now. She makes within a minute fear to bravety and pride !

She sounds lovely !

Yes, and she has sometimes that roarrring in her body that starts from her nose all the way back to her end, when we enter the market, that tells them all that she is here again. She really enjoys to communicate.

I bet ! Missy doesn't like other animals so we can't take her anywhere there are other dogs or cats !

The Fishermen always knew it.
Those peaceful places we chose in the beginning years, when she was so small, they passed the shore and threw a few fishes to land. She altime found them and had a very good meal in her stomache before going home.

40

I must just close my eyes and feel into the night, the black in darkness and sit on that ground with others around, say no words. I do always keep it with me, and I still do realize it.

That gives peace.

> "May the stars carry your sadness away.
> May the flowers fill your heart with beauty.
> May hope forever wipe away your tears.
> And above all may silence make you strong." - Chief Dan George

Rest and sleep. Get closer to You inner Child. I can make it share in small pieces and I know I will only have steps to do without forgetting the context and the concept you need to look at my back so as not to forget my identity, to have a good trip, my Dear...

"Good things come to those who believe, better things come to those who are patient, and the best things come to those who don't give up."

Feel a bit lowtide but that's winter mood.
Whenever we talk I m lookin forward to it.

Yep Winter gets me down ! I love our chats too !

That is exactly the point I reach today, too. Let's leave it like this.

Yep rest and relaxing.

Lovely those animals can sleep everytime and everywhere.
Then once after a long trip they be awake they give You orders what should happen, and see them watch You now and willing so strong !
There is too the small kitten that wants to be a tiger.
See a real painting of a husky ! It is so beautiful with every detail, even those eyes. Nature's beauty is just build to fall in love with every creature.

I do everyday ! I adore nature !

Let me think. I saw young those horse eyes like a mother. I grew in strength by the billy-goat. I woke up of my dream by a tiny pinscher. I had my first brother in a labrador. I felt first mourning by a dead blackbird that could nomore sing. I loved and adored the wild pigs smell who enjoyed to cuddle in the mud. I knew myself in looking in the eyes of the lynx. The eagle showed me his pride sitting near my way and wasn't shy. The seagull showed me the sea on my run away from South and let me feel the salty wet in the air. The crow are flying together and protect those at night on the search leaving a town. The bear is the one who is there in loneliness.
The worm wants your help in need, and warns You of the danger, not to get swept away. The ants are a childs friend in the woods, hiding and being everywhere. The bison doesn't care the human, if the human doesn't care of him. The dear is a strong natural protector, in starting to talk to You to leave a place that is not good for You... And so on and on !!

I meant of course, sorry sure the Dear does protect ones heart.
But in nature is it the Deer that starts talking if it is necessary.

Yep Winter gets me down !
That is exactly the point I reach today.
Let's leave it like this.

Rest and relaxing.

This one Woman who talked so long with me once some time ago, she talked about living in Ireland or Scotland. So I defitely dreamed of driving around there in a white car, watching out for a place in the country. Then we left the car and went across the green hills as long as we reached the place we seemed to search. Somewhere outside, no town, no car, something like a railway I think, and an old small farm.

I feel it ... there starts my fantasy again, so I have that cribble in my veins, as if soon a new story has to be written ! No problem ... my head does that work himself ... I ll sit and be brave ... and let things go to be done..

Yes, of course I would have better my child should give birth on the island, it is said that there is not much stolen there. Then maybe I wouldn't have the child stolen from the puerperium, just because few scrapped junkies denounced it. So why they did it and sneaked around my life ?
It was to demonstrate, they could force people to believe, so they hoped, with all kind of pain the woman broke, then she would help them to press others in churches name, she would have no one talking to, no ones nearness as long, as she would be another one, that knew better times, but I never forget, what that was to survive with a straight heart. I was altime strong enough to deny, and fight against that fashism. I was never in stand to work for their deepest wish. I was so many times before consequent enough to think about that. I was warning the church once, to think about the Child in future. I was warning many times, at last I grinned them in their faces. I was never in danger, because I knew I kept real love in me to them who I thought they needed me. They gave me no work to do, never mind. I worked all this years for the weak just for free. Of course, I could have asked forgiveness on all fours, then I would have been offered an assistant position for comfort, limited of course, with the only exception, if I let myself be made pregnant again by anybody, who cared who it was, to be considered a birthing machine and possibly one day, they play the game on people with the wrong promises, maybe I got a job at church, acting like those, who rigorously goes against all forms of anti-social abuse. But to do that I would have to join the Church and offer a few more children to official state abuse.

They didn't even think one moment, that I was worth it, to continue my very own valuable way, that I could do much better things than them ! Who else would come along like that and would be an honest woman, who has nothing to ask about work than me ?

I recognize in this story some unfortunate situations which, even when they are organized by a handful of individuals, are unfortunately too followed by stupidity and selfishness by people who do not know what to do with their life. We often meet this situation or it is those who are afraid of the king, who throw the first stones at us.

In the history of humanity, the powers seldom used the force of the people, because it is much easier to reign over ignorance and stupidity. In this context, we must remain discreet so as not to awaken among those whose justice we have not known, the desire to deny and denounce our difference. To live happily, let's live in hiding and live happily to live in hiding.

Have a nice day.

I ever knew that Love is possible.

Indeed.

This man I knew was out of stand to feel real Love to Women. He just marries her, then another one, he takes them like they lie around and he just picks them up, and leaves the next again. He never was worth it as a friend, so even the others told me and took me beside, never think this, because he is an Ashole in real !

Someone told me to.
I have stored Food. Its called storable food.

Now I ll have soup for four days long. That's seldom, because I don't buy meat so often anymore.

It is a long hard winter now. We feel the coming spring.
But we still need to have enough food, not to start to freeze.

I am too freezing.
I was one of those people in this city
for whom life was made difficult for so long
until I was also tried
to be considered an ordinary alcoholic,
and to despise accordingly,
without touching a drop !

When I learned how to convert the fear of failure into the opportunity of
failure, I developed creativity, flexability, agility and the ability to explore
new ways for achieving my goals. A wealthy person invests first and spends
what's left, while a broken person spends first and invests what's left.

You have to be naked far up, you can't even see the smallest enemy in You
giving up. Would he recognize that your counterpart was like you ?

Those believers tell around they would mourn and play games, turn you the
back, wait until you went off, and then hold their fingers on you,.
But the worst is, this are priests from church, and they try to hide away, that
there are our kids on the school yard, who suicide and they just tell the kids
on a show off that they hated kids.

I love apples and usually eat everyday but not now -
no teeth so only applesauce !

That is really funny, Carrie. Might really be that we could have had in
former times the same neighborhood in Ireland near some Apple Trees ....
hihihi

Looks Like This Virus Is effecting a lot of Humans.

We shall rise upon all human weakness and to show the new way to those who is still lost within the darkness of so seemed for them no way out darkness. We did now its fine, and I made me a big pott of tea and she has captured the warm place under the blanket herself, but we two enjoyed it very much.

I am studying body paint now. I ll have to learn. But I learn by doing. The more I try, the more I learn. Next year they will be much better. But I had to find a start, so I could imagine the bodies better in my mind, and now I try out all those moves they do. It's a funny game. I love it.

Carrie, You have more pains when it is cold. She showed me a pic with all these body places where she suffers. I better understand chronic suffering. And needs to smoke Marihuana against the pain. I imagine to be such a Warrior. Such a great Woman.

Hi, Carrie -

If you accept him that heals. You need the warm flow of Love find each place inside and get befriended and stop a war. The same You love the whole world. The same You must love each cell in You and stop the war. Each cell is in light. It is yourself who can heal. Maybe now it is time to heal yourself. And too there are steadily thousands of real big Buddhist Monchs who do healing to the whole world and all liveables. There is a medicine Buddha helping. He is blue. And too Daikinis, who are female Buddhas with lots of Love. You was altime thinking of others luck. See You was altime strong. That power You gave whole life, was to take away their sorrow and grief, their mistrust and fear, their sadness and poorness, their negativity. You see ? You do have that buddhistic skills, under Your skin ! But it is all Give and Take. They way You took there dark clouds to safe them, you did Good Things. And Your heart collects Your Good Skills like Your light from the deepest inner side from Your heart. This is Your energy

You send to all. And this is even Yours and that Power that gives You the ability to heal. Each Buddhist meditates on this, to take away now that dark cloud of Your problems in his breathe, then takes it to his heart to his light and breathes out sending the light directly to You - with all those positive Wishes for You that You need !

So it goes. Its easy !

Lollo Pigalle. The woman is always alone, likes to show herself.
If she doesn't, she's not good. She doesn't read a book, she pulls herself out of illusion, she languishes in shame, her charms have no name.
She is not a beauty, but knows how to sell, everyone can have it.

She saiad, the espresso pot has fallen down and has a hairline crack. I hate problems before espresso. It is snowing, as if dreams are falling from the sky. As if gray is turning into nothing and disappears in puddles of melancholy. This is another morning, dear ones. I would not sing for you !
I don't keep myself open to you. There is no love for this. Hello.

The weather - still subtly gray.
What a missed shine. What misery.
They wanted to treat me badly and abuse me.
They wanted my dignity.
They wanted to prevent my ability to love.
They wanted my ability to find a reference to the past.
That's why they took my child away from me.
They wanted to cut the phone number to all memories.
They were more men who hurt me.
They still lurk today to fool me into a wrong world.
My family acted towards me.
The others always ready to turn me into a rope.
Those will never understand that I live quite well without them.
Since the older I get, I find that they are different.
That they will never understand me.

47

It may have been difficult for a woman to define her feelings in a language that is mainly used by men to express her. But I can now look into every little crevice of my existence, and to bring this up is not a particular feature. The raven's power animal sometimes gave me this special talent. I wish everyone else too.

Good Night !

Carrie - You are so charming. I too love You.
I too love and thank You for all and wish You Having a Super Day !

I am so grateful for having you join my journey through this lifetime !
Your insights and charming spirit are inspiration to me !

How do I integrate spirituality into everyday life ?
Throughout the concept of "spiritual life" and "everyday life".
There is only life undivided and whole. - Adjashanti

The purpose of religion is to control yourself, not to critizise others. How much am I doing about my anger, attachment, hatred, pride and jealousy ? These are the things which we must check in our daily lives.
−   - Dalai Lama -

Thanxx today after the walk with Mable I ll hunt to supermarket, so I am sure to have enough in the fridge if that Virus will enter town.

I am relieved you will be preparing to shelter in place !

Then we spend a good time together afterwards.

Yes, and this famous business man still holds the line, because he wants to superwise me in a kind of business plan for me. He gave me a free explaining to understand better financial prinicipal words.

That is a lot to understand. But maybe I find a start with his advice to make something real !

Synchronicities

Yes there are quiet many of them ...

Yep I always take notice of them.

The same that happens when I write too much. I altime know there are those others who think similar to me. And human conversation spreads worldwide. And those small novels be creative but too inhold the most adventures behind what I already lived out. And I don't know if I continue how much others then will start to head on my boat and ride away in fantasy.

I see a lot of 11:55 and 1:55

That tells me all live is such a fantasy ! I see here many cars, they might be all police cars, because they altime come from that street, they own the number 11 11. And once I was waiting on a cold winter day to wait my bus to work somewhere, when we stood and waited, and one lorry passed by so slowly with the written words in a looong sentence, that said "The St.Pauli News" this is our biggest Redlight in Hamburg, very famous, but I have never been there....

Wow And you imagine that big naked lying woman on the lorry looking to the passers ...

I saw a police car drive by with my mother, father and brother in it, I was 7.5 months pregnant at the time, my brother was dying !

Heavily. I was getting raped in cars twice.

I couldn't realize the driving license because of that.
That is seemingly the reason why I am afraid of the stress of that word
"Fast" that I do drink liters and liters of warm tea every day since thirty
years, just to calm that word down, and let the warmth, slowly flow, and
then flodd out in a small quickly sprinkle and relax with it to get rid of
something that didn't hurt, but makes me happy like lively water.

I can understand that !

This makes me sure that there are many doctors in a womans life, like the
WATER, the Breathe, the Heart Beat and Dancing Feet, the Heart in
everything and everyone that lives, and the smile in those faces of all them
who know about it.

Yes there are !

Goodness there are really many.
Those Ravens make me sure, they understand me better.
Those Seagulls give me motherly protection and warmth.
The crow send me back to Childhood time.
I do take a rest never mind if I get tired sometimes.
I Love You.

Love you.

Can't promise I'll never complain again but walking behind an apparently
happy man with a prosthetic left arm and amputated right leg you realise
just how good or bad life can be.   - Lox Graham

"Black in America and Loving it"   - David Cummings
"Never second guessed my own instincts."   - Shepard Fairey
"It's exactly what I make it."   - Tom Simonson -

Sweetie Can't You sleep ?

I managed to fall back to sleep finally! Thanks.

Its so good to feel winter still like he surrounds us in this far quietness. And it makes me so proud being with existances like friends, just people who are able to live easy, with less like many, and knowing about the sound. Sure is that I am just talkin in a fantasy english. That made you often laugh, but that makes it funnier.

I am ready now to understand what that gentleman means. He describes me to make a financial Dashboard, and then see if I do household good, he wants to explain its on me, what I can put aside and how to invest in my small part, to make more of it. I read it to the end, and then I make a list of income and in what I spend the money, then make a future plan and an aim. He might check my list then, and give me advice, and that is just for free, someone like a father from afar, who tells me it's exactly what I make it, sothen there might come a financial change, and if I don't it's my fault.

I shouldn't altime make the mistake to look back, behind there is always that voice tellin me I ain't worth it. I just start to think from now on - It is MY BEING, without that mistake to be arrogant. He talks about good vibes. No one wants to end up financially wealthy, but leading an unhappy personal life, which can be empty from strong family ties, strong relationships with friends and the community, healthy bodies, and spiritual development. His theory is lend money and make something out of it. But I think this might be a real thing to think it out !

I don't think I should lend some of it, if I didn't have a good job in the backround.

No, it's not your fault ! I am going to invest in myself as soon as our tax refund gets here ! New teeth, hair, massage, facial, waxing and I will start the year fresh and new ! Courage, dear heart. Keep going. Everything you need will come to you at the perfect time. Tough times don't last. Tough people do. You have to be at your strongest when you're feeling at your weakest. It is during the hard times when the 'hero' within us is revealed.

Thanks I needed to hear that today dear friend.

Our daughter's new Australian Shepard Whiskey came home yesterday !

Wonderful Beautiful Lovely Awesome Handsome Great Alive !

Yes his name is Whiskey.

And he looks a a bit drunk !

Lol sleepy.

As I remember Mable as young, she did relax only a few times, she found out wild things to do, this seemingly tiredness is deceptive.When Whiskey ll make to know the other kids, he will turn off pretty wild.

He's already met them and the other two dogs.
He's bigger at 13lbs than Jack at 11lbs and Bailey at 5lbs.

That's good. He is the smallest in the family, so he has fun.
I see the other both are smaller dogs ... and Whishey might be biggest.
That's funny ... a biggest Baby !

I will see what my Son will tell me in the coming two months. This is his very last try to finish the college. Let me wait, what if he will manage it finally ...

I understand.

My Son is doing his own. I might be lucky if he just told me he finished school. He enjoys telling me anything. This is wrong he just tells me about once in the year anything whatever. But he is doing well how he wants.

He knows to follow his instincts as long as he needs, that he can guess what life has meant for him. So Why Not ?

Yes once they are grown they fly free and only so often check in at the nest !

Yes that should it be. I am happy to.

I am happy to know that he didn't fail as young in this province in Schleswig, where I be this second little guy who was bullied he killed himself ...

Of course you are happy sorry about the second little guy.
Yes, I do altime feel when someone dies earlier than me, that I would have lost some brother or sister that I loved.

Sure I have always remained true to my loved ones, but I determine the future, how close or how far they are from me ! I felt a lot more and much closer to many other people than to my family, at any time, for example there where at least people that I cared for, healed, whom I assisted in grief, who I accompanied in their suffering, who I supported cognitively, who I warned of self-destruction, who prepared for the future, comforted them, assisted while being pregnant, simply listened to them, reconciled them, ...

Beautiful.

Yes, these are the ones who come up to me in their natural way, that they see, who does feel love and would give them the help they need.

I just tell them that the love they see in me is the love they have in themselves.

That's Big Love !!!

Like one would say.

"There is never a reason to be afraid, but a reason to be prepared !"

Yes, Sister.

We are going slowly out of winter now. Today I walked with Mable two hours, and still the sun is shining. Maybe two weeks more, and then it starts into spring with warmer temperatures. I still wait for the day, when the ways are no more muddy, then I start the jogging training from new. I wait for it.

Yes me too I am so sick of anything but Summer time !

Yes that life in a big country with climate like yours isn't just a honeypie. I feel that your husband is still listening what we share.

March 1st Source Message

Tell yourself :
„My body and mind are purifying. This is a detoxing phase of my life. At the same time, I am learning to seek less, and allow more. I don't need to have every step next figured out. I will allow my energy to lead the way and not be burdened by having to find direction. I am learning to navigate between physical and spritual. This path is creating a sublte feeling of wholeness. My life is piecing itself together with intention in each new day. I have everything that I need. My mind, body, and soul are in a state of fulfillment.“

Great I ll read it again and again.

I know what You say.

Certain people with limited mental perspective very often restrict also the view of the others. Especially females are used to be belittled and now, when finally more or less equality became main thing in society, even if not always we see it, there is still men with strange mind.

That's altime the way it goes. It is the one way we move. Out of town, town behind, back to town. And see them drown. But see those work for it but starve. Them run across our feet would never apologize. More sit out there in the rain and have to freeze. They want our money today, but they would never do the smallest favour sothat we better come along. Old times are gettin lost. New have already started.

I really saw life on the left and on the right. I walked in the middle of it and watch it talking to a girl I shared once my thoughts outside. There I saw them altime get drunk, in their dark rooms outside the crowd. Left behind one town. There I saw them work as slaves, most women, work for nothing to rid away other's dirt. There I saw those years when my son grew in the sun, but now he's flown. There I saw them sitting outside searching for a place to hide in the nothing, in the cold and collect some wood to make them a fire. There I saw me in an old house, what just left my memories and nothing else, with a lawyer that was at all out of stand to work on the house and wouldn't do one favour, because he knew that his rents will appear on his Dashboard, that made him rich and nothing else that mattered to him and wife and family .... That dream made me and my compagnion girl on our walk open us the eyes ! Now I see the more unlucky and the more living in luck, the less of all human behaviour not matter how rich or poor they be !

This I had dreamed last night.

You see, this was a number I was working to reach.
I have published in ten thousand pages within about a hundred thousand different thoughts that I have raised on the subject, and have achieved well over ten thousand of my own tweets in the past five years, and for a round just thinking about the times I recently described on 111 pages.

And the Good News... Friend Arne from the danish border Flensburg had an eye on the danish schools, because my son Julian had his try to finisih college on a danish school in Denmark. So Arne told me that Denmark has decided to give them kids a chance to get their college finished by fill it out just with the tests they already have mastered, but this year just without an exam. My son seems to be on holiday with his girlfriend and be pretty lucky about this. But I didn't hear of my son since three months. This is an optimistic news, I thank for very well...

This real rich man wants on March 20th have a talk to me. I surely know what he wants to make me believe. As well as I know that I won't take money from strangers with the promise he made me well rich. I am aware that normal ways here around tell everyone who won't be able to work at some place won't have the chance to get a credit for example to invest in immobiles, because so suddenly they tell us then, we were not allowed to own money and we are in the guilt of the state to pay back what he gave us.

Here is my situation. I Am Chanceless.

This is my guarantee, that I am not out of stand to care.
I do care for my Love. It's sure, that this is not my fault to live poor since I know it. But I have the well thinking and knowledge.

Looking deep in the yellow eyes the boy replied,
'I am more scared of my own kind, than I will ever be of yours.'

So You're sick Carrie ? You could stay in bed, but I removed the fever in two days by putting cold envelopes around my calves. And even if you don't want to, you have to drink a lot, preferably with lemon juice. I relieve coughing by inhaling drops of eucalyptus twice a day with a towel over the small saucepan. The pain and fever will then go away in a day or two. If you also have almond pain and runny nose, inhaling with peppermint would wipe everything away in two days, and snuff plenty of towels so that the sinuses do not become blocked. Wait patiently until hunger returns, then reward yourself with anything that comes up, maybe a hot milk with honey. That seems to be a long hard winter for You.

Thanks I use these same methods xxx

Okay, then You are not alone.

No Bob is home today.

Mable was out with me, and she took her first bath in the water today, nice she got her nature back. Ah, yes fine makes me happy that Bob is there for You. I love this so much.

I remember outside on our way around the castle there stood usually a very old tree, but we saw the last storm has overtuned the old one and his trunk was completely hollow on the inside, and had hardly any roots lef.
This makes me sad. Another brother that has died.

So sad.

Yes, but the workers for our small wood see it easily. They leave the trees naturally. In that small place may the old ones lie around and disappear with the foil. This is no straight park. This is a home for all trees and birds and eagles we have. And for kids who like to trust in nature, if their mothers go its paths. I find peace there. There you find your ancients talk.

Yes I go to the woods or the sea to replenish my Spirit !

Yes, I do it in a kind of communication. I wait for something starting talk to me, a deer, a crow, a raven, or other big or small birds coming very close, when we are alone.

In the rain I am sometimes busy to put those beautiful worms back to the soil when they left to streets, I find them very beautiful, too.

Each kind that You can safe, is another kind of knowledge You win.

Yes that would be lovely !

You are a true Heart, Carrie. If You meet a deer it would protect You, if You just sit down and wait.

Then imagine that might be another kind of Woman in Your heart that looked into Your Eyes, mentally and quiet and full of Love, with her Acceptance and Healing Power, that she would never ever leave. You alone as Woman, because she notices in watching You the whole damn Life You've been through, and then You might tell them what's all about it.

This might be a mentally Woman. And she was always there.

Yes I would.

It does.

We use to say altime "Moin Moin" here like the Danish say "Good Dau" what means at each time we say it here to everybody day and night time "Hello, welcome Good Morning" even at midnight and to every cow we see.

We are not just poor plants that grow lonesome without the others good wishes. We are not depend on our family here as much as you do. We are awakening each morning altogether in our whole big beds and everybody knows well then, the other wished us our best, if we do so too.

But this depends on some kind of nervosity and feeling for the words that lie in between.

True.

Yes, this kind of nervosity is meant a bond between them in the countryside, not easy to explain, more without words, meant not to be naive, meant more to be sceptik, but the more you trust in you, then they trust in you. The sceptism is needed to divide between the narcisstic ones who treat just good their sons, in a pride muster to be found everywhere, and the other kind of sensibility for things they might not be repeated or done to another liveable like any harm that has been before, that is the healthy way to say "No" to things here. But there is none who describes this, until You understood.

So true.

Yes, this all might be truth for some and for some others don't.

Sadly not yet.

But there has come some comfort and peace in those minds.

Hi, Mister Chammas !

If You have a second I ll explain..
You are someone real rich and want to have a talk to me.
I surely know what this wants to make me believe. As well as I know that I won't take money from strangers with the promise he made me well rich in five days. I am aware that normal ways here around tell everyone who won't be able to work at some place won't have the chance to get a credit for example to invest in immobiles, because so suddenly they usually tell us then, we were not allowed to own money and we are in the guilt of the state to pay back what he gave us. Here is my situation. I Am Chanceless. But I thank You for advise. I already learned from beginning to household with a minimum since long time, because I wasn't that lucky to get a work in what I can do good until pay the rent. Now I am no more young enough to try out hard work at other places, because my back doesn't work that good. And I wrote. And I detoxified many times. I learned a bit of English. I do have friendship relationships. That money that I may put aside is in the pay for a small amount to help my pension. I am depending on the state to supplement my low pension, which means that the state demands every extra amount I earn back, including my income from book sales. I cannot invest, firstly because I do not have a regular income, and each money is counted as income and immediately expropriated. I am also no longer of this

age to take such risks, to have someone else tell me the tip for risky business relationships that are said to promise wealth in such a short time. I see you admit, the way to wealth is only paved for those who come from better circles and highest wealth thrown at the feet without making a performance. To me, all of this sounds like a badly ending fairy tale. Since I have lived a meaningful life and draw my conclusions from it, I am aware that as a writer I choose other platforms to offer people my personal advice based on my life experience through a slow process. Ultimately, earning money from my books only depends on whether I manage to develop a level of awareness and that over the years. Because I do not belong to the privileged clientel, who is prominent at first, and then make her few written outpourings a bestseller with just one name. My success depends solely on my performance, and I have been feeling free enough for a long time. And I don't dream of goods, I live drug-free, I don't smoke, I feel no need for alcohol and in my home I think I am happy alone, knowing that I am different from many others who would never accept this or even denounce it, I sought their community. Don't anybody tell me it would be never second guessed my own instincts, like Shepard Fairey did. I altime in my life know it's exactly what I make it. And so it is good. Being Writer, Artist, Mother, Single, Lifeeducated means for me to trust in me and none else. So please, Mr. Chammas, thanks for advices, but I believe, we don't have to go deeper into the matter. Thanks for all,

The gentleman answered -

Hey Heike.

First of all, I command you for the crystal clear clarity you have for your life. You are really blessed to have lived a purposeful life. I would admit you are among the very few who are privileged to have such a life. God bless you. It's also quite a great achievement to have written such a large number of books. Would love to learn from you on how did you manage all of that. Given your current situation, I would never have recommended you invest money or pay anyone for advice. I fact, I could learn from you.

What I wanted to suggest on our call is that you leverage what you have written and your audience network to become a coach in your area of expertise. This will provide a stream of Income while being purposeful.

You could also join hands with other authors on a new book and leverage their audience. Regards.

I think -

It's the truth too. That this all depends on my own, what will be. He honors my abilities and my way of life. That is beautiful. But I see the real work starts now, from advise more other people in how I do think and write in a Network. I already wait for this. The3NinesArts offered me several times now, that this membership from into their innerst staff is wanted. But I do still have to wait for the start until April. This network shows all good Artists from the whole world. This made me glad, to be real a part of all this, and I would be sad if the platform doesn't work this out for me. They already loved my paintings.

You're an amazing writer and artist and I believe in you ! You can accomplish anything you set your mind and heart to !

I am looking forward to what You say. Yes, now to be patient. And summarize helps too. Maybe soon more people expect more from me. But that is the way I wish to be active.

Between Spirit and Earth just a brave Heart
like You living with a vulcany heat under skin,
and still walking along like them wandering on the Edge.
It hurts knowing about your pain.

You have it nice there I mean is Bob near ?

No hc's About 500 Kim's away at work !

You can be so proud to have such a handsome man out there like a lion !

To live with pain. This is a sign that Your life is stucking. When I was in too much responsibility, work, household, puberty, homesituation, No one near to help, My beginning of writing, ... that pressure in mind pressed my back, because I had no relax and I noticed to get active again and so started with fitness. That held me strong eight years long to live fit and without problem. Finally the years as a single woman in a new appartment with an allround activity, so I healed my soul. That was the point that all my backpain disappeared ! It is just a sign of coming out of the stucking hole and move again. You are not old as long as You don't act like an old !

I believe the one or other has a problem with this.

I definitely don't act old.

I know my Dear, I know about it that Women are the real Crouts who never act still and stuck in Life. Some people know about that treasure. I think this is the main reason because Your Husband loves You so much all life through. I do tell You if I was Your husband, I would have married You too !

I don't like our mentality.

I understand xxx

Don't feel bothered, I am such a clear thinking, that I am sure that Frank now is upset for my answer. But I say the best friendship must hold with true words and free telling. I would not accept a relationship to anyone anymore, that would want me to pity someone. That is too old. Younger women get abused with this. But I am really out of this.
Like You taught me not to apologize never, and have no shame to tell true things. I ain't that character to relate my opinions, there is my character, that I imagined myself before doing such things and really start to laugh out loud, because I saw in my father's face sitting so below that he would be the

very last, that forbidded me my opinion ! I told him, that none would explain him to keep that feeling to be young in every age, if he doesn't try himself.

I said - Why do You think to be another today if You are just as old as You do feel ? No one would be able to give You that feeling to be a part of it, what meant enjoy to be alive ! Nice, that he was active young, but I said - Between extreme fun and usual activity in willing something like a ride up to a mountain and getting real tired with it are two different types.
And willing meant not once alone, but many times training from small to better, but not extreme. An extreme diet doesn't work too, because the time after to fall in the trick to eat definitely more and get lazy extreme again. There has to be found a balance of it to enjoy and to train.

Balance is a key ! Like I think You would have said.

Yes each muscle thanks every time that I use it, and makes me feel, so why not use this feeling ? I met an old man in the wood with two old dogs, the one was a dachshund, who was waggeling his tail to us from far so friendly. And we came near, I told the small one that I would be so amazed to meet this kindful Bigheart and thanked him so much. You know what he did ? He acted like a little duc and sang a real bird's duck duck duck in all kinds of octaves - just because he said, this kind of speech is possible, and it makes everybody happy, so why not use it ?
This is a real kind of optimism I think, that we have to learn ....

I also believe we should all be active.
When I am well I do Hot Yoga with my daughter.

Yes, I have to make a soft gym on my bed before sleep.
Then I didn't need to pee at night, but it altime works.

I want to make a yoga area in our new home when we move in 3.5 years !

Our bodysystem, each use of muscles, for that the flow in our lymphatic and blood systems work hand in hand, so the poisoning can flood out, and that stoff is getting rid. I am sure the movement in the cells works better the more we give them things to do, like a car that needs to drive not to belong to old iron.

Yes a modge podge of things make up what we are.

And many small bacteria too.
We are such an animal, but at least only few know it.

Yep We are !
I must cook supper now ttyl

We also have another brain in our intestine, that works on how we do eat, and controls the main hormones for the best those hormones who help our mental health ! Ohh Yes, Good Apetite my Friend !

Thanks xxx

What will happen to the dream that never lived ?
Does the sun dry him up like a grape ?
Or does it swell out of the wound as pus ?
Maybe he just loses balance
or simply explodes.

Who ever likes to marry with the first smile of someone he never told you anything before ? And You travelled And You saw them people from everywhere with every age and color in their faces. Then she comes along and plays the Bigheart, but she only chose a prince with the everlasting smile. There is no fairy, no prince, no glitter, no mirror around her smile !

What I do love about animals the most is they have another very kindful and very special way to wait until you feel good.

I know them who think being human means something better than being a dog, or a cat or a tree.

When I was a child I had a fever
her hatred pressed me deep into her crevices.
I had to rise like a balloon.
I had to fly as far away as possible.
I saw how many resigned to the world instead of mine,
driven to death because they saw no way out.
Now I have that feeling again.
I can explain it and you wouldn't understand it.
I talked about it to my child,
who are comfortably deaf have built the wall,
the wall that surrounds their hearts.

Ice melting underneath another layer of ice surrounding a tree. The single most important commitment I've ever made is the one to meditate daily, any effort to live our best life has to start with time alone for self awareness and reflection.

3 AM is the hour of writers,
painters, poets, musicians, silence
seekers. overthinkers and creative
people. We know who you are.
we can see your light on.
Keep on keeping on.

Your positive role in my life and empathy give me trust and faith, it is your universe to guide and create synchronicity. I ever knew through giving, I recieve. Through loving, I am loved.

Hi Carrie !

We are having pulled chicken sandwiches on pretzel buns and red cabbage cole slaw.

Interesting idea. I love it to see how much fantasy you spend in cooking. When my son as very young got something warmed up in the microwave, but he was out of stand to touch this, he didn't accept that food. I saw an awesome reaction of the child, so I thought to be warned, and gave the microwave other people as present. Everything else the child ate ! Since then I don't touch it anymore.

Yes microwaves kill all the good things in the food.

But then You fool Your body, spend all the money to buy, all the creation, the herbs and taste, your hunger ... but you would eat something dead ? That reminds me to the soup the Nazis gave them in the hospitals to the clients, to starve them to death with a soup that was cooked for hours and had no ingredients anymore. You see, they all died !!

But these narcisst creatures expanded the degenerative idea to study on dead people, the most of them where children, orphans, the disabled, the homeless, foreign children, the unwanted and those outcast by their families. And they told the society there they would educate them to better people, so they would welcome everybody there. Such a children hospital I find lying in about five hundred meters away from my house.

Meanwhile each old nurse coming near to me, fears that I directly feel her sweat and fear and tell her directly into her face, that I know where she once worked, and ask her then smart about how she thinks about suffering ?

They really don't tell something against and give to know, that that profession made hard, so that they were able to accept the death around and see that the most didn't really suffered, because they died sometimes quick.

Yes people want convenience over quality.
Yes my Opa was there !
He was in a concentration camp in Czechoslovakia !

Yes, as you say, there are Germans who are too easy to pronounce Nazi atrocities, whose deaf ears are everywhere, but whose grins on their faces openly show that in these times the woman in this country has been taught from early on, her first shown smiles only when she gets a ring on her finger, no matter who would be the one to look after her.

This is the reason why they were allowed to all of it, because of their women who were too convenient and deaf !

Sadly yes they were.

Brrrrrrrrrr !!!!

But every criminal has something to hide. And he feels caught in everyone he looks in the eye. With this knowledge of his aura, I only have to guess from a distance what his name is, who he is, and in what radius he is thinking about other people, because their fear of being discovered, their cowardice, as with schizophrenics, is widely visible ! My answer follows just that path, as if I talk to an one eyed type...

Just breathe !

Let me know - was The Grandfather Your Hero named Mr. Nightingale that one Grandfather that spend his torture time in the concentration camp in Czechoslovakia ?? He looks so fantastic handsome and smiles with such a strong character right into the camera !

Yes he was !

If we had not him in Canada, We had not You, My Dear !! Fuck that.

Actually he was my step-Opa my biological one was Swiss/French.
Roger Gideon Hammerbeck.

Okay that made it better for You not to bear that past on your shoulder also,
I think You did bear enough of all.

No not that past.

But this young man looks pretty too into the camera.

Yes he was too xxx He died early, but I didn't know him. I only knew the
man that was my Opa Nightingale.

My Goddnes. I mean sorry. Yes.
I am proud of You. That is Good to have known People like You.

If I sat in the South of France now with some friends outside under the
starshine, we would build a huge fire and put a whole pig on it and eat it all
up, I promise. It's enough.

It sounds delicious and fun !

Yes, You do love big fires and good stoff like meat on the fire.

Yes I thoroughly enjoy it !

This is a very seldom joy, but it's fine.

Yep.

The only thing that holds me here in winter with many housekeepers send a smell of firewood in their livingrooms. When we walk then we just seem to be near of it.

I ll go ahead and watch a film to calm down.
Good Night my Sweetest !

Now something funny against the hype -
Germans loot business, they buy pasta and toilet paper. Imagine you are in your hotel as a vacationer and at night someone knocks on your door and wants to measure your fever. Globalization leads to supply bottlenecks.

I know it will be a Pandemic as I have had prophetic dreams about it for years.

Imagined too once in the dream just the masses.
Certain minds might be clear way to knowledge, where people fall, those like you rising up. It is wonderful to own a clear mind, a healthy brain, a sight of the reality.

Sorry that early time. I didn't want to disturb You.
Don't worry. Be happy ! And sleep well.

Thank You Goddess for my Sisters.
Have a blessed Day – Lady Ravenna -

I still have the winter in my bones. But we start with longer walks.
I see too everybody needs resting, and specially animals here around need a while to get used to all the light that is presented.

I met one woman she was on a walk to visit her brother. I met a lady she really remembered Mable's name and had such a happy kind looking. I met two Men who held an older Mongoloid man in their protective center, and we had a lot of fun. He hugged us, and he proved, everyone was given a nice slap in the face for the hug. But we were delighted to have him among us !

The Mongoloid are altime spontan, and take You in the middle then check them all up, and want to be the middle, so such an appearance is altime a spontan feast, better than any sandwich you ever ate !

The plant spirit is hidden in a shadowing cupboard all her life, inside of a tiny small bottle. Inside is her perfume. That name of it is her secret no one knows. But she comes from the desert. There the sun altime shone. The nights were altime cold. She has hidden all her questions for so long. You ll never know for how long. And because of all those years the passers treated her with misrespect she had no time to rest, she had no time to ask one question, she was never invited to open her conversation. So don't wonder, why I sometimes have many questions to ask...

And i will Be short of words. So ask Your questions !
And I will Surly answer Them In Little words.

It is not mine who walks to seek for wisdom. It is that wise living to wait until the wisdom appears itself. It will be that day when I ask the one, and it will be the time when I ask another one.

These interests of others force me steadily in answering quick. But I see too many of them who produce their questions in hundreds of forms, then spill out their coins in front of me. Then I think that I am not stupid, and they should buy some good books and don't tell me to be friends. Then they do really lie and tell they have read my books, and I ask further and see it is not true. These are the ones who are blushing, my Dear !

But the younger they are and ask such a mess of things, I tell them they should finish school first, then learn, then work, then know the people, and maybe at last they might understand how the writers of all the books think, then they might right their own.

The less that I talk to humans, the more I speak to Mother Nature, the more the animals freak out when they notice me. I scan my environment. And the spirits have notice of me. The more I let them equally aside and my body speak the better are my dreams.
Yes, I do, and I know I can't.

Talkin in real. Not too much magick.
Sure I confirm your awareness is a pretty magick ! And Your Eyes still try to command. But I am in my world of magick, that tells me not to bow another ones Eyes.

But I Would Love To look In Them.

Yes i do look in yours.

Hello Heike, I'm sorry I didn't reply to your previous messages. for me it is necessary to regularly pick up communication systems to have a clear vision. The current context of the epidemic is causing inappropriate behavior. The financial world fears this situation, and at the same time speculates on human stupidity. I think that the big question of this phenomenon is the breaking of the barrier of species. Already, SARS and avian flu had to alert us for a long time. Among the living species on this Earth, the human being shows signs of weakness on the immune level.
I wish you a good Sunday, and may your dreams remain intact.
Sincerely, Alain

Hi, Carrie !

I just got back from shopping with Bob ! Never again during Mercury Retrograde !!! People are obtuse atm !!!

I agree on the observation of animals, we were there not so long ago, on a human scale, close and in cohabitation with the Bear, the Wolf, the Wild

boar and the Master Deer. Nature sends us a message through them.
We must continue our occupations like them. I wish you a Good Sunday,
and may your dreams remain intact to our WOMANS DAY !

I WISH YOU A NICE WOMANS DAY - and it will be a nicer Year
for You than the last one !

Today is not a holiday. Today, like every day, is a day of struggle.
Simply that we make it visible today, scream, dance and even with a smile.
This fight is fair and for the good of mankind.

Like You love Your Sisters too, I do thank them too. All of them.

Today I decided to invest into Avira Safety for one year, allround for both of
my PC's. It is the best thing I could do. I see the effect, and Good Service.
It was a good idea. Before I used the free program of CCleaner, it works still
like a program to find the Tools that are installed, to install and uninstall,
and is a good kind of window for that. I used the program of Windows
Commander for so long years now, that gives an insight in every partitition
and does connect the one to the other and copy and organize very clear, so it
does open files sometimes that are out of stand to open in another way.

Yes the paid ones are better.

These are my cupboards that help me very fine out. And even my second
notebook, that is safe now too, and even those many sticks they store my
privacy too.

Yes I love organizing family folders.

It is very good to be organized.

Yep, I am a Virgo so I love any organization tools.

This meant for me too, that I have to talk about each decision with my beautiful dog. She listens and she waits for my clear information.
The pauses in between meant that I have understood.
I bet Your dog misses the same talks between You and Her.
They play strong roles for me, all the animals.

I talk to my dog everyday.

Now that all updates have been recharged, I can report back. It went well.
Even my little notebook with Windows 7 seems to work like never before !
It is the credo to find out themselves, but not to be shy to ask the true friends for advice.

Now I can show You my favourite recepts at my home ... There I can show You the file I use each weekend before shopping as cheap as possible.

Potato salad
Vegetable and potato soup
Pumpkin soup and meatballs
Chicken soup
Chily C. C.
Lentil stew
Lasagne
6 way salad - with 6 eggs, 6 potatoes, 6 small apples, 6 sour with -
    cucumbers, mais, ham, yoghurt, mustard, olive oil and vinegar
Filled puff pastry
Spagetti bolognaise
Spagetti mushrooms, leeks, cheese
Casserole
Fried potatoes, sausages, e-carrots / cream cheese / peppers
Matjes with -
        boiled egg, pickled cucumber, bell pepper, apple, mozzarella
Grated cake, apple puree
Goulash
Shredded meat
Celery schnitzel
Pizza, cheese
Cauliflower, potatoes, cheese sauce
Rice salad
Sunken eggs
Green core meatballs

Cherry bread pudding
Custard, raisins
Baked apples Vanilla sauce
Muesli fruit groats
Fried egg on bread / kohlrabi / spinach
Chicken fricassee, rice
Fish fillet, rice
Spring rolls
Tomatoes, mozarella, cheese, balsamic vinegar, olive oil
Salad, mozarella, tomatoes

Thank You. Thought I was over the bug I was fighting but it seems to be lingering in the background. Flare Day too! Staying in bed resting today. Won't be on social media much. Love you all !

I can't get out of bed. These blankets have accepted me as one of their own and if I leave now I might loose their trust.

I already told You this. But now I did it again.
I agree the virus and oil war has created panic !

It is not altime that reason. If we notice that all belongs together. But if we are not confirm in how they do, then of course at the main point their habits reach, means they will fade away like others will have to do it, too.

I do love more that version from You, that protects the old and the weak...!!!

Freedom in a democracy is not a crowd of howling boys who think they have the freedom to choose between schnitzel and potato salad. It arises where the perpetrators bow to their former victims and participate in their reparation and dealing with the past and stand by their actions. Because the freedom of the victim to give a name to the injustice does not keep the perpetrators in a kind of calm, because this calm is lazy, just as lazy as the church, which abuses children en masse, but this is considered socially. Like disabled people, who are administered but are the oppressed, whose economic misfortune deserves an economy, like their army of people who show no interest in their well-being and human dignity, and the farce with deaf ears, simply because it is more convenient, and this is well paid. This shows that the majority is sometimes an asshole, but it is the small rarities that are allowed to raise this in a democracy.

People say it was just a suggestion to double food it if you can afford to !

In my opinion you can keep your money in self made bread, cooking for two-three days, keep some stoff, but don't get in panic.

That flu would mean that the stores would close. I don't go through town for a while, don't visit cafés, walk around where are not too many who use my ways. Maybe I buy some more beans, rice and noodles, tuna, oil, parmesan cheese and buttermilk. But that is just to stay calm and not to go shopping every day, like many do. People don't know to keep their money together and buy often, but don't make a plan. But it's okay, because I do know, these things they store now aren't these that I would need. It is not the reason to hide, as long as you are healthy. So I am shopping on the market on early time to get my fresh apples and my dog's food. But I saw there are people nowadays that buy very disciplined on the market. I wonder. I did travel around in Europe as young about eight times, and never I thought about getting full.

I even didn't need to think about food. I saw others eating but I was never asking to get a piece of it. But sometimes I needed water to drink, or went into an orange field, or grapefield to have some fruit, maybe few of biscuits or some beans help through the day. I too went to the bakery in the earlier morning to ask for a few rolls for free. I sat in the restaurant and watched them getting full, then leave the plate with the rests. Even in a university where these students get filled and leave their plates aside, for the luck of those people just go ahead and eat the rests. Many years I heard some ate from the rubbish tons behind the supermarket. Today young people use the Apps they tell them this or that shopping mall or restaurant or bakery gives them food at the end of day for nearly free. Other places people work for free, and giving poor people bags of food, that came from the shops. I knew with a small handful flour you can bake some small bread, use the herbs grow outside and put some tomatoe from the tube on it, baken on the fire, ... that is delicious !
Nowadays I need medicine, so that I might go sooner or later to my doctor to get a new recept, that might hold for a while, could be intelligent.
Yes, tomorrow I ll go. I didn't think about that.

Mister Chammas !

Your public work is amazing.
It was kind of Your seldom information,
that I never believed, that I didn't know before,
how easy it is to get well rich, if You get the chance.
Please No more newsletter !
My personal freedom is more important.

But never mind. I know I am a writer, that includes, that I have got a message to tell. No matter how poor or rich my readers would be.
If am getting mad, because of Your newsletter, that meant, excuse me don't send me advertisements. But if You might forgive me, after a walk I cooled down, so let us just have a try for a talk on same time we chose.
I ll go to Your calender again, but do not expect a wonder. I am just a bit in panic, if people from afar tell me about the wonder earning money or to be "welcome in the Millionaire's Club".
I like to invite You, just to have a look onto my publisher's website Books on Demand, even found on my website heikethieme.de,
where You find right on top the link to the Bookshop with all the german and english books and push the cover for a free look inside.
You might find my 22 translated English books and You could read in them 20 beginning pages for free, to have a look in some of my thoughts, and You were not forced to buy them first.
This is just an invitation. And to talk with you so far, made me a bit shy.

God bless You, in Your words

Wil gladly look into your page in the next 2 days.

Don't worry … fully understand your frustrations from my automated emails and newsletter. Rest assured … I will never try to sell your anything. I removed you from the newsletter mailing list. I will wait for a new date that you will book in my calendar.

Take care… H.J. Chammas

Hi, Carrie ! Do You know what makes me mad ?
That Censorship no longer stops at books. Whenever I want to turn a
booklet into an e-book, it is checked whether I present many naked women
in paintings, and so such books are not wanted, and okay one naked Man
was within too. This is Art ! Never in the old times people censored the big
painters for this ! Yes, that is awful. Then there might be books to
worldwide they won't appear maybe without that I know it ... like You say.

Just imagine there were no more Artist Painters Fotographs Graffity
sprayers Dancers Theaters .... without Nakedness ?

Then they could find another terrestial species with their Gens and DNA and
scientific immature madness, immaturity and mediocrity testify to how
narrow-gauge the human being can be, in the ego limited to a sum of
Characteristics, such as reputation and appearance, like I jokingly often
would say, "I am" and only singularly describe it as "me", finding
everything else as interchangeable, at the same time individuals are
simultanieus, unique and interchangeable, and only in its personal identity it
the ego limited.

Nature is not what is embodied by man. He imagines himself to be as
powerful and threatening like nature. Nature can be an even more amazing
role model if man did not believe alone the way to find her back. Nature did
not create art. Only art imitates nature and then it replaces nature in man,
through his reflection on art. An optical flow itself decieves a lot, and if
every single human responded to all the stimuli differently, if man alone
often stands still. He rarely learned the proper course to survive that he
countered in the team, in a tremendous wave of nature not to go under.

To tell about Art and Nakedness.
The censorship of the works is a foul hypocrisy, while the means of
suppressing the pedophile images implemented are not up to par, the
algorithms of the controls on nudity in art aside from works whose purpose
remains artistic. It's ridiculous ! We have the example of Schyzophrenia of

the system in the United States, which on one side advocates puritanism, and on the other side remains the first provider of pornography.

I will never be politically correct, because "Politically Correct" is already a form of censorship.

This is very true.

Carrie - You altime tell about that Flue - Do you get in panic ?

I don't know, maybe that goods cannot be bought, that medicine is no longer available, that people are knocking on the street, that children are no longer able to go to school, that the job is at risk, or something similar.
With regard to Covid 19, we can see that no government in the world is really ready to face the situation. Unfortunately, panic situations are fueled by the media and do not have the impact it should have on the population by making them actors and responsible.

Saturdays on the market, if those good people who are sellers, they test the customers, and wait for the answer with a smile, asking if they now wanted the double of it ... I could scratch me with laughing.
When I step into my favourite Danish Library I start to say Hello like everybody does, then I shake hands with telling "instead of it doesn't be allowed" and I do share a "Good morning" and I forgot the time. And the nice woman still standing and being secretful and sceptic I came in my library since more than twenty years and I do still have the feeling, here are most people discreet and don't jump at me with sympathy and don't slick my breast.

Yes, it is altime Good to know those different languages.
Do not have uncertainties. This will hopefully return to normal in a few weeks. I understand your reaction. There is always in the functioning of the human being, the part of analysis and reflection which is his without influences and on the other hand, the collective functioning and its rules in

which we cohabit. It is precisely here that discernment comes in.

Good Morning !

It was to be able to dream. I had an old wisdom to follow the spirit child in the dark wood into the cave under it to talk with the smal creatures and follow their way to be proved ... to prove my heart, my reality, my bravety, my social skills. Then I saw and found the answer, that each question is to be found inside and none else. To my own wishes.

I know there might be everyones nature. But none is innocent. I know we can find our protection and our middle in nature. But if we don't know our roots, we live a struggle in life until that day, we start to connect our ability to our inner system, to live in a system with everybody. Like in former times there were the old people who taught this to their sons and daughters, to be worth it, and nothing else was truth but this in heart.

If there were so many who suicied with strong and weak reasons, it was me, who found the strength to confront my long past, and finally found to the real kind of tears that could give me a sense and freedom to be free of mourn and pressure.

It started with my meditative calming and sat on the floor calling out for my inner strength and the answers to my questions. Then I had to let work my fantasies, and I wanted to go the way in writing down to connect peoples' wisdom and experiences and build out a developping examination to get to the innerst point to understand myself, like a little doctor in me.

Now its okay.

Things in Italy are horrid with this virus! Much worse than the media is saying someone told in the media !

This will return to normal in a few weeks.

I don't agree I have family there !

Weather is cloudy. In Europe there is climate change now. In Spain it is nearly beginning Summer and has 35 degrees. Here it is weather of end April with weather changes every few hours, ice rain, sunshine, storm, sunshine, icerain, but cold. This shouldn't be. Spain will start to have a real heat problem, and we find spring is less and summer will too start very suddenly, then it will stay warm until November again.

See, these are hundreds of languages telling all the way the same, to be wise and look behind, say hello, but not to be naive. To be critical, sceptic, secretful, wise, to guess who is it before knowing him. To live a life presenting the own style. This is the European Principe !
And based on the frightening, mendacious capacity that the Church exercises on us, we should at best pull this away from our children to believe everything that someone else says !

Happy tonight. I am not shouting anymore now.
Good Appetite ! I thank for Your trust.

You're welcome ttyt.

Europeans are diverse, that's what makes them everywhere. So from small town to small town they are proud of themselves and change their spoken dialect every fifty kilometers. Then just imagine how thousands of dialects in this country and in all 20-30 European countries could have developed their own mentality and sign language among themselves. It would be very, very stupid if every village began to differentiate from its neighbors !

I am happy, hurting and healing at the same time. Don't ask how.
Being an Empath and a Sensitive the chaos taking place right now is taking its toll on my nerves and body/health. Can't sleep well, no appetite and anxiety to beat the band !

Tell me and I forget. teach me and I remember.
Involve me and I learn. ~ Benjamin Franklin

What a difference a new skill makes, the importance of correct breathing.

Don't let yourself be controlled by three things :
people, money or past experiences.

We are not animals. we are not a product of what has happened to us in our
past. we have the power of choice ~ Stephen Covey

Blessed are the moments, the millimeters and the shadows of small things.
                    - Fernando Pessoa

Leaves of light and dew foam, color sources that chase every sound.
                    - Paul Eluard

I took my feet to follow the sun, then shook my head to understand and
think before I told, then jumped over stones and roots and bushes through
puddles, until I stopped. Then painted on the stones, cooked my roots, used
the herbs from bushes, and took a bath in those puddles, and sat where I felt
good.

Smile whatever You can do ? This is first time people meet in sorrow, and
notice their is need in everyone. But You see, none helps another when its
getting dark outside.

"I dreamed, the most beautiful dream. I take flight... and I flew !"

Song of the Drunken Man -

For example, you could dream of ....
the crowd heater claps for you alone,
since we know that the viruses go to sleep with a clear conscience, and if we
have been facing each other since the Stone Age, then also that ladies kiss
and celebrate our old people, that they are still alive.
However, if people brewed a cup of tea with the shower water, one would
have to consider that they are drinking viruses. Now that all children are
celebrating school-free, the worry that nobody knows what to do with their
own children.
Scientists gradually run out of details, explaining to people what happens to
that. Small shareholders can finally thank the stockbrokers who gamble
away their money because "Fear - Food - Stock the Market up !"
Small businesses offer short-time work benefits and are allowed to borrow
indefinitely, so that hopefully only the poor will get enough food.
Uninhibited emotion, euphoria and racism in the football stadiums have to
take a break and nobody pisses you off. Football fans now wander idly and
disoriented like zombies through the streets, who now their own wife have
to serve for the replacement situation.
The old white sack's brain has been in quarantine for years now, and has
long had no clever thoughts in it, votes for including no Europeans, and the
27 million Americans without health insurance will surely stay healthy.

The old white sack's is much more concerned about the Dow Jones Index
than the health of his own population.

Good evening Heike, while the 2008 financial crisis was the result of excessive and immoral speculation, this time producers have been cut off from the grass because they will lose much more than they could earn in the past. hope soccer fans find other occupations more rewarding and less mind-boggling to occupy their minds.

A little quote from Paul Claudel: "Only solid is the one who relies on permanent things" - Have a nice week end !

Stay as Genious as You ARE !

This is no ones only fault. This is a serie of bad happening all around the world. Sure this is very sad for You all too. I love so many elderly too, and that makes me so sad. But You know Your president is shouting bad about us Europeans, like we would have caused the problems in Your country, sothen we were no more allowed to enter the States with exception England, because of Your business connections. This is laughable enough. But today he too came crawling that he might be willing to buy our scientific workers and patents, if we might be able to find that stoff against Corona. You See what Snake he is ? He fools around but evil like he his, he just wants to make a good business with this !
Here You don't answer.

The expansion of the new antennas is ongoing this year, so I can try it out in peace and inform myself. If necessary, I prepare the whole apartment. I just need an idea how I can cover the whole silver foil with something white so that it doesn't look so hideous and what I do with the small cracks and window frames.

Your welcome Dearest !!

That State of emergency. Many are sick but elderly are dying.
This is no ones only fault. This is a serie of bad happening all around the world.

No some don't even know the difference between a patriot and a narcisst. And don't tell the narcissts is doing right. Some relevate all his destruction of rests of democracy. Most seem to be blinded by his run around American heads, but see the Poor don't even get food by him. The weak don't get medical help they really need, so they can die. The students can't afford the studies. The woman will not be able to abort. The democratic lawyers will no more act. The police gets brutal. The wildlife gets killed. The landscape get robbed for industry. The wide world business gets interrupted by his nationalist ego. The place he owns he got by lies.
The millions he earned he stole the state. The dangerous slaughterers in other countries are his friends.

Let me have a part of it what shows your opinion. I know that Americans have their own view, so they might tell it with their own words. However just because other people around in the whole world see this different, you may resist on your own. Tell me more, if Your in need telling me your words, I don't mind.

You See ?
She said all beings can be safe.
but their sex should be better off than the masses.
She said so everyone has enough reason
to celebrate their lives, to be happy,
from this privilege you have to appreciate their individual lives,
honor and always respect.
She said to protect all of this a solid wall was needed around their city,
and a cavalry that protected them from intruders.
Nobody is allowed in who is not healthy.
Nobody is allowed in that does not contribute to their happiness.
Only then can people be free from suffering,
when they realize that they united all cultures,
who act, live and think as they do.
All beings should follow this, their ideology,
otherwise everyone would be in trouble !

2020 will go down in history as the year in which politics and business have had to admit that professions that have been known for years for lack of staff, low esteem, unpaid overtime and comparatively low gross wages are systemically important.

You live in Quebec, my question is, do You understand French ?

Yes, we are mostly all bilingual.

This is nice to know. I thought there are some strict talkin in English.
That tells Your lastname, because he is french. That means to me, that french understanding people and French from everywhere do have it easy to understand me, and I feel a real existance to whom I talk, without all that improvements. I mean it is better to feel accepted than altime wishing to be friends and regularly people let me fall. And the norvegian ones of my family I only knew as young woman for a few of visits long ago. And that gave me that strong feeling to have chosen to live alone, but to feel mature and powerful, like my laughter is. This I would never change anymore for anyone !

Yes Bob speaks very little French.

Nice thing, like me, and little Danish and little English, but I ll never give up learning more of all the people !

So I am trusting in French and in English, and I am laughing in Danish, but I am philosophying in German.

I mean I can see some of Your Good Old Friends on photografs.

Yes because our family will remain here at least for a few years.
Does that mean, that they would follow You then ? But You had the nature and wildlife around and You had a husband with lots of time ... that might be enough. Something that I ll never have ! GOOD LUCK THEN !!

You too xxx

Spring arrived. Today we walked, but tomorrow I do have the new season and train jogging from new, but it will take some time, and now the climate is wonderful, sunny, windy, warm and fresh. This will do us good.

We all need to thank the truckers out there working long hours to restuck stores and gas stations, like my husband Bob who is high-risk and should be home self-isolating.

Yes, I thought that. Has Bob health problems like You too ?

Bob has Diabetes II and High Blood Pressure.

Oh What A Fuck !

Another thing. I'll try to keep the 5G radiation out. The simplest trick that can be used to seal off the radiation in your own home is with self-adhesive aluminum foil for walls and the ceiling, and self-adhesive window film. It's cheap and I'll give it a try in my bedroom. The expansion of the new antennas is ongoing this year. For being real safe of this I already use from Vivobase, that firm also exists in America, that stick to plug in, that fills the air with a small kind of electricity, sothen my skin is uploaded and builds a shield against the 5G. And I noticed the much better going along since that first night I used this, and finally slept again since twenty years.

I hate 5G.
Look at the percentage of Corona.

Yes, and I hate it too, listen and hear about so many serious deseases that You do have to fight, but too You worked and raised the kids and had a nature around that did not altime do You favourites. Now I see how big weight Your Life was to live with that big time making compromisses all those Years !

To care - to love - to bear - to share - to feel sorrow

Thanks xxx

I do See that You own a Good own family, with a strong bond. And this is for me a kind seldom to see that Man hold on to their Wife and Kids. I enjoy this, and I have learned a lot by knowing You, so I thank You, too, Carrie, so much.

You're welcome xxx

This is the first time in my life, that I notice Men hold on to their things they are befriend. I did know just german types of Matcho, liars and concurrents at work, informers, storkers, ones who suicide. Now I make to know real NORMAL PEOPLE !

This will be the finest Year in my Life !

I am happy for you !

I understand. There is always a good reason for new aquaintances.

Love you xxx

That day of my interview with Mr. Chammas. I am writing down what I ll talk about with him about my working, living life. I chose the interview of Margaret Atwood from Canada, she talked in a very beautiful way about life, like that I will talk, too. Maybe this is my try to talk with rich people like they sat with me here, and just talk about the weather.
It is not the reason to feel shy, it is just the try and see how it goes !

Then today is jogging on the plan.

Spell of the day. Spell for grounding scattered energy. To stabilze your energy, fill a small jar with soil. Then call on mother earth by chanting; Mother Earth solid one Kissed by rain, wind and sun. Bring stable balance unto me, As I will so mote it be. Keep the jar close by - in your purse or at home or workplace, and nervous energy will be no longer a problem.

A negative mind will never give you a positive life.

Some look in the mirror. Untamed does no Art look away. To see the most beautiful, and the most awful, and never to look away ! The past kept our good remembers, so we do just talk about the beautiful. I read in four languages. And Peace will be because we have the choice !

Like we say to stand to our children means, they were made in Love and nothing at all. And if we stand to our children, we let them decide, even the daughters, because they are not our own ! But what makes all the forbidden things to come to the surface. The Illusion of time. The way of material, that will never be gone. I move through the rooms together with You in time. So my watching my past, is my travel to the origin, to a point from where everything was in order, so then followed all my written pages to get together what all was to my order, to my book, to All my Written Books as long as it is given to get my steps into my past, as long there will be the reach to it.

Today was jogging day. So we ran through the windy rain outside the city to the hardware store to buy a universal spray bottle.
We stood there in the garden department wet from rain and a nice man behind a two-meter barrier, and the protective tape around his table advised me that no flu viruses wanted to start him. He grinned and was just imagining how I ran home with my spray bottle through the rain to water the flowers in my garden. But he looked up at me seriously and beautifully from a safe distance and asked which of his models would suit me ... the small one in pink for a ridiculously low price, or the chic larger version, and then this in two versions, with lever or pump. I looked at the chic models

and answered spontaneously and firmly that for me - as a wife and mother, the seller thought, since such a practical pump also served as a breast pump for fresh mothers - only the pump would be an option . Then he carefully handed it over the barrier and I cried out, "No, for heaven's sake!"
He thought everything was too late now because viruses were still coming. I said, "No, I'm sorry, I only have the change for the cheap version, so I'd rather have this one." So I hopped happily to the cash register and he called after me if that was all, and who was taking care of him ? But I think if he hasn't died laughing so far, then he probably still lives tomorrow.

Unfriendly Tweets nowadays use to make people afraid, me too. And I already do know myself to keep my head up to sky. I don't need to crawl for friends and feel manipulated, in that direction of extreme thinking.

I will have to make a pause with them who need me too much to care for them. This is work to do and not my fantasize. I can understand you to need someone every day not to be alone, to feel his shadow, not to feel sad, to feel his shoulder, and who makes you laugh, when you wish to feel happy. But I am my friend inside first, that detouches, when friends are going too far.

I need rest and peace for a while, and this depends on how my friends do accept without judging me. Never mind.

Well you have to do what is the best thing for yourself.

Yes, You are right, Carrie, because I am that far. I do have to know what is going on here.

Those people get loud easily.

But then I meet those young quiet and friendly mothers with young daughters asking me everything about the story of my sweet dog, and I love to answer every question, they thank with the eyes, and this makes us happy. Then one young girl with her two brothers and an italian Mastiff, and we too love to talk about Babies.
Then one man he altime walks alone like me since years, and doesn't talk for one whole year, but today he talked like a waterfall, and I could give him each answer he wanted to hear, that I saw his longing for the love of his wife, and I saw him run home to be with her, them start to fly home into each others arms again !

I am so happy that You and Bob and the kids now are really safe.

Bob is feeling better today so he goes back to work.

I bet now to follow Your heart with all the fears You had, as long as he fighted there...

Yes.
I ll make tonight meditation that he might come home soon.
I ll make it safe.

Thanks xxx

I am untamed. The Artist never looks away. You have got to see the most beautiful and the worst. You may never turn away ! This is illusion of time.

The essence of matter, that we might ask is the three-dimensional World nothing else but illusion ? What we need today is empathy, solidarity and mutual friendliness !

"Though all people are allowed to think, many are spared."
   –   that said Curt Goetz.

This my Dear I saw that morning. We two walk along the small city since a month again. None there, but the one Woman, she lives downtown and cares for many and talking, that she has gone over a big desease like multiple sclerosis, but now there has been found a real medicine to survive. And she still walks and talks, but she is altime looking in people's eyes and answers with an ironic sense. She stood there in an empty city, and I had to laugh, like town seems to be dead, but she steadily stood in front of me !
But I told her, she shouldn't be afraid of us, I wouldn't lick her off. And still the Germans have the privilege with supermarkets each two kilometers, and won't need to work for their food, and could get fat, without caring for other people or get in danger with that ... so on my opinion we Germans never would get compared to the rest of the world that has survived in holding on together and risk their lives for another.

Shall I or Shall I not ? I am still hiding, maybe too shy to talk to that Mister. Maybe I don't because I learned to keep the circle small and not to trust in strange Men with a lot of money. Who ever knew what this kind of people did with my interview ? And I am realistic, that this one of person won't be the one, who solved all my financial problems .... What Will You Tell ?
Is my instinct right ? Okay I decided to cancle that meeting.

Follow your instincts.

No, I am not shooting my careful and warnings up to the moon. I had a special warning in my dream, not to leave my roots, because too many Good People and My Son hang on my opinion and awareness, not to give my principe of life away, because of a hollow illusion. I do better protect this.

Many centuries of mounted warriors including the Scythians, Huns, Vandals, Mongols and Middle Eastern warriors have used effective forms of light cavalry, striking terror into the enemy. The sources suggest, however, that the vast majority were awake and facing the right way.

So we should start riding our pig !
They always said "Had a pig !"

Any activity where the fun is stopping should be suspect, so why go running when it feels good afterwards ? If the transvestite says he is trapped in the wrong body, I see, I am trapped in the right body. No one feels comfortable in his body. Wouldn't it be to promote absolute immobility ? If no one knew in the morning which foot is known to be the wrong one, it is better not to get up with anyone. So I, who is in a friendly relationship with her body, would also find that it is probably up to me to compost it myself one day, if I consider myself a case of care.

Well, we know, people sometimes recognize ...
that we are all very diverse, and especially since we have our own individual toilet, so that would prove how easy it would be for us if they had their own sense of humor. But nevertheless why doesn't it work that they would drop their pants themselves with laughter, but always want me, who knows how to laugh, to have to lose them in front of them all ?

He is grumpy, annoying and anti-social. Firm candidate to be a friend.

Madame is recommended.
Space affects my run through time.
Lightful smiles are better than the hussle not to come.
Who read the news got me my favourite.
Just stay like this grumpy, angry and distant,
these candidate might be friend honesty,
so I always have a reason to live as a free woman.
Couldn't be nicer to leave the beautyshop longhairy.

But knowing the recipes who to get angry with arguments.
No matter is better than hang tight to the Good old Times.
Was always suspect to those who were lazy life passes fast.
No way to get to the middle earth without start the orderly state.
Expand and continue of this is never to find back to your roots.
But who serves with scary threatening and never told open dialogue,
what matters to him, without doing anything for another one,
he might leave me alone, he might stay alone again,
if he chose not knowing himself.
Once the chances are lost, but the sky is still blue and eyes can see.

My best tip of the day:
On the one hand, you shouldn't sell yourself below the price,
but you shouldn't even sell yourself for the biggest money to the world !

Based on my life experience through a slow process, depends on whether
I develop awareness over the years. I do not belong to be prominent at first.
Success depends solely on my performance.
I have been feeling free enough for a long time. I don't dream of goods.
I live drug-free, I don't smoke. I think I am happy alone.
It would be never second guessed my own instincts.
I know it's exactly what I make it being Writer, Artist, Mother, Single,
Lifeeducated, to trust in me and none else.

So please, thanks for advices, but I believe
we don't have to go deeper into the matter !
We have something in common. But we can overcome that.
If a woman has her limits that she interpreted to exclude other women.
Who uses the stimuli physically to sleep up at all levels to be successful.
Where far and wide no man would be available to stand up to their
intellectual standards ! So the woman was enough to use the vagina for her
position, where today's woman would just HAVE the vagina and not
because of the old days !

Today, however, tensions also build up due to unexplored sexual needs that people shoot wildly and throw themselves at the feet where one woman envies the other's looks or what she can do.

So my bucket list said -

Make up !
Kick ass !
Repeat   !
Love x Life !
Respect !

Often you cannot say
in these days
if you leave the house already or late,
when the sun goes down ..
How late can my love be ?

The three things that I think are important in life
are love, a task and hope.
Only women who run to the barber every month
who think it's more important to go out with a bra only,
who confuse the pride of being a woman with mare biting,
who prefer to look fake from behind,
and fundamentally change it every few weeks,
who see their bodies as a kind of punishment,
from which they must never escape but shape it,
the new creations that make them up
don't let air, water or combs rule,
would strangers say that to them, complain,
they killed you for accusing you
that your criticism is appropriate only if you were friends.

I don't need a wild hairstyle.
My hair would never matt.
I would never sell my hair.
I wear my hair long forever.
Nature gave me the most beautiful hair.
Like tacit funding
and for the wrong committed in history.
This means just a little translation to that
what Men have done to me !!!

Why does the German treat women
as if because of his mood of war
to dance a smooth rumba for men
although men have never become men
based on their actions ?

It is time to stop worrying about what we were and thinking about what we
will be. They continue to politicize everything and try to blame the rest. If
we don't unite, we will never make progress. Sometimes I think that the
virus of this world is us ... Only when everyone has understood that it is a
decision that love must be above fear and hate, only then will people have a
chance in the future.

Giving thanks to life,
giving thanks to one heart,
giving thanks to the sacred space,
where everything is possible to express.

- Estas Tonne -

It's time,
that people will rethink
that their fear destroys or breaks everything
but that love must be above everything.

Your quarantaine nickname is how you feel right now and the last thing you ate. - Yes, an apple a day keeps the doctor away !

The universe is full of magical things patiently waiting for our senses to grow sharper.

If you're constantly telling anyone who'll listen that you're an alpha male... I'm pretty certain your not.

Gyms closed until further notice. Take the dog and jogg.
Now they look each other in the eye.
Then it is fucked until the walls shake.
To do this, sweat until there is no more water in it.
After all, everyone lacks water in their eyes,
which is why the contact lenses are no longer floating.

Now there are options
how others envy their food,
shut down old iron and mines,
licking breasts under the sprinkler,
dance in front of the window ledges,
clean up the garage,
make the world upside down,
to drink the ugly counterpart,
dust off the old flail,
imagine the dance floor for yourself,
try to hop up the stairs,
after the sun slip into the lowlands in the North Sea,
the neighbor with the cleaning devil in his hand,
Kick Ass,
then knock him out of his socks.

Now I'm just fed up.
You're turning me on !

Come to the toilet with me.
Why, I don't have to.
What does your star sign think about making children ?
Ask your ascendant if that's possible.
Little one, you're just looking for the fireman
but the fire he wants to put out is yours.
You know, if one of them might want
then the other cannot because it is not possible.
So if you wait outside pretty,
you also get your ice cream from mom.

This is our universal house -
come in and have a look.
It takes in everyone and all neuroses.
You will love it, step closer !
No matter, even man is always the same here,
as you see - my wife -
but the technology can fulfill all wishes!
Whether warm, cold, light, dark, crumble cake or sex.
Good who longs for pure nature
we offer the perfectly reproduced ant, all in gold
or the talking dog.
If it's not enough for more imagination,
we use the ladder over the attic,
and come as if we didn't live here.
You will see, the kiln will - uh -
be the milestone of our future !

If all scientists would Love to punch some politician in his face for just
thinking of his business plans for future, for example for the business sell
medicine against flu, but cares for no desaster he causes Now, and has no
better plan, than let them all die, I do understand them better now ! It is truly
a very sad story and global that made me cry, if I had known all of them
who have left us now. I wish there might be some fewer who own the same

books in their shelf at home, that I own too, and that this desaster will end
soon. I am recently yours and will ever be !

Let me not to the marriage of true minds admit impadivence.
Love is not which alters when it autorotation finds
or bends with the remover.
ever fixed mark that looks on tempest,
never shaken,
the star to every wondering bark.
Whose worth unknown although its height would be taken.
Love is not time's fool,
though rosy lips and cheeks,
within his bending sicco' s compest cup.
Love alters not with his breif hours and weeks but bares it out,
even to the edge of dune, if this we error and upon me proved.
I never rid no no man ever loved.

- Patrick Stewart -

The marriage of two true people.
Love is not there,
where the spheres move,
swirling in the flow of air and water, winged.
No less, but through a number of poor decisions,
overconfidence and reaction to external determination.
Not to be found where there are obstacles.
Not related to the one who moves away.
Love is an eternal brand,
that looks at the storm.
Love is never one, it is shaken. That's what I say !

- Heike Thieme -

It is truly a very sad story and global that made me cry, if I had known all of them who have left us now. I wish there might be some fewer who own the same books in their shelf at home, that I own too, and that this desaster will end soon.

Yep Me too.

All businesses except essential services are ordered to shut down by midnight tomorrow here.

Yes, that is what I need to know about love now.

Yes, that is the only and finally happening in this world. I only do feel sad for all those poor places in the Orient, in war, in whole Africa, in India ...... Brrrrrrrrrrrrr.

So true sadly.
And I tell You this will take a very long time til its end. We won't have any rest. This stillness outside is cold. That world lies in a sick sleep. The elderly and vulnerable be in fear for sure. And their friends too of course. Thank You so much for this Mr. Patrick Stewart's words about Love. These are the wisest words I heard for such a long time. He said these describings so pathetic slow and carefully that everyone who had a bit of English in school-class can understand !

Lovely.

This is such a true kind You talked about yesterday, that our energy shifts move and change us and our environment with the moon small and round. Yesterday I was strong thinking, my head was a bit dull, my sleep lets me work more, I felt a little breathing problem, I loved to eat all time, the nose was running, I felt a bit lost, the world outside seemed like a dead world with danger. I felt real exhausted But when they pass in the wood from far, and I shout out the name of their Babie by name, she suddenly turns and gets reached by my call, even her Mum doesn't want it, bearing her unkindness and her face without a smile. The stories about Angel numbers in my life still appear, and synchronisities make is easier and easier to look through the relations of people. My dreams develop to let me see through decades.

That I could say that this Book VI will be my blessing to those, who have clung to me and encouraged me not to lose confidence.

When times turn better we might have together one Ginger Ale.

In real You Kids – it's all forbidden ...
No Smoking !
Drugs prohibited !
Alcohol prohibited !
Switch off mobile phones !
No knives in school !
Nazis undesirable !
No batons and pistols !
Don't wear baseball caps !
No e-bike on the premises !
Not roller skating !
Racing across the hallways prohibited !
Don't run barefoot !
No dogs on the school grounds !
Don't use a will and throw people !
Do not wear headphones !
Don't pee while standing !
Do not wear combat boots !

Good evening, sorry to not have been on twitter, but the current situation forced me to turn away from the web, to bring my concentration and my support to the most vulnerable people. I read with interest the messages and images that you sent me. I see that your philosophy of life remains intact, despite the sadly dramatic situation. Communication with our fellow men, which is usually not very easy, has become practically impossible, at least in a physical way. It is a demanding test for most people, but it is surmountable! We must think of those who provide services and care to the sick and do things at our level that help improve the lives of fragile and socially isolated people. We must also be careful in our dealings with others so that we can continue to help as many people as possible.

I wish you a good evening, Best regards, Alain

Thanks that is very true, in one case we are altogether maybe infected and people even fear the small kid in the street hold to you his freaky tongue, as if those kids now were the disease themselves, and say "Now we can't say, that everybodies kids are our kids !" But would these such good and loyal people in normal days go ahead and give some handicapped neighbors their guarantee to buy the food, if something happened to them ?
These busy altime working people might be the last in the chain once too, and who would be there to help them ?

Wittgenstein was always in the park at night
having sex with different men. Was he afraid ?
Did he generally want to be left alone by people ?
Should he deny his own story in this way ?
How did he manage to draw the line under it ?
Did he think he was on a path ?
Was it his will to free himself spiritually ?
But the path itself is the goal of defining your own philosophy
and understanding it.

IN A WORLD WHERE FEW SPEAK THEIR HEARTS,HEART YOU DO
SO WITH THE PASSION OF THE WIND BEHIND YOU.

FORGIVE THE CAPS I HAVE BAD EYES AND PLEASE EXCUSE MY
DIRECTNESS.I BATHE IN YOUR WORD. I WEAR YOU.
YOU SEEM TO SEND THIS VAST METAPHYSICAL EMBRACE.
I KIDNAPPED YOU IN MY DREAM
I SEDUCED YOU ON THE SAND
IN THE EVENING AT HE BEACH
YOU GAVE ME THE WARMEST EMBRACE
SUDDENLY I FELT A POWERFUL RELEASE

I need to describe this in more than a thousand pages !

What if the universe is trying to get us slow down ? To stop producing.
To stay home and let the earth breathe a little without all the extra pollution
we cause daily. To take a step back and realize how we really impact earth
and one another. That we aren't as significant or in control as we think we
are. A virus can come through and wipe us all out but earth will still be here.
We are all connected. Just like we can spread a disease, we can also spread
love, kindness and positivity. Use this time for reflection of your
contribution and the life you're living. Slow down and finally hear yourself
again. The universe is always speaking to us if we are willing to listen.

That is what I say. Smile to everyone. Without thinking three seconds
before. Love Your neighbor. Help the handicapped. Send Love and Recieve
Love and Stay Tolerant as You want to be treated tolerant, too.
The "individual in the crowd" is the doubting one in the tight. But that was
yesterday. Today the individual stands in the void and feels abandoned.

Sincerity is the most beautiful exercise of loyalty that two people can give
themselves. In my life I set the rules and cheat when I want to !

As much as I tried
the earth gave me birth,
I had no name
no other religion i hid to be part of my earth
and breathe their air
my nation is the world community,
I never knew a race,
so the spirit protected me pointing the way.

Well, the man has it just like that,
invented the wheel and the associated car,
to use it as a chariot for his wars,
to prove to the world,
he could rather kick the whole world in the bin,
until nothing lives to show,
he preferred that,
as mother earth itself !

We see the spread of the virus also has positive effects.
Initiatives and neighborhood assistance are emerging all over.
Companies develop creative ideas sothat they can continue to be there for
their community. You keep an overview and nobody feels left in the void.

This virus knows no nationality no religion and no skin color. Suddenly we
are all the same. Maybe we'll take that with us in the future, because I hope
for a learning effect.

A french woman told me not to try again show her an Eagle and never tell her about hunting. I told her to know about that, I already told even my family not to try to forbid me my mouth, and never try that again. I learned to know Native Indian poetry, then I travelled, then did a lot of things and learned by life, now I follow the news of the world in English, Danish, German and French, just a part of it, and of course I met here nice people from all over the world, so did translate many into English.

Germany is well known for fairytales. People who lived in America when they were younger told that the Native Americans have much wisdom.

With each of us is a brilliant spark. When ignated it raises to the surface like a shooting star ... a burning nova for all to see.

Wild Woman.
I'm a wild woman. I trust myself. I never need to look to others to justify my actions. I move when the moon moves. I live by the light of nature. My nature. My soul. My truth.

I burn with divine energy. People often wonder how I manifest my dreams so easily. My mantra is 'I was made for magick'.

I'm a wild woman. Money is my fairy dust, and joy pulses through my veins. The present moment is my enternal home.

I care for my fellow wild women. My tribe. My soulsisters. We help each other arise. Elevate. Leaving things that dumpen our Goddess. Nature in favour of building communities, that live so loudly no one can deny their magnetism.

I'm a wild woman. Howling at the moon and roaring with laughter. Sitting quietly to listen to the song of my intuition. Wandering the world with big eyes and an even bigger heart. Refusing to censor my soul. I speak my truth every single day. Because of this I am free.

I would be interested what kind of help You do for Your neighbours !
I wished to find out what kind of relaxing You and Me prefered.
Perhaps the crescent moon smiles in doubt at being told,
that it is a fragment awaiting perfection ....

Instincts like them trees merging with the bedrock showing the alertness
and hunting instincts which make it an apex predator.

We know what it meant how to fear the one You love the most. When you
don't know the danger, you can't fear. I wish You and Your family the most
peace and luck to find out of that crises, Frank ! And of course I am much
worried about You. But here I meant to worry about the one You love !

Carrie ! Your are right, stay at home with Bob.

I was aware three years now. And times do change for all.

This silence outside makes me remember that our country could have much
more space than I thought, space to spread the wings and fly, laughing
inside, but too joking to suprising appearances, because people do react so
much more intensively and open for spontaneity, this a strange days, like
walls are no more walls, and seasons, daytimes and minutes passing are no
longer a matter of course but a gift. I too see, that the parents seem to be
more relaxed than the cool kids.

Friend Jay from California is infected, too. I answered to him -

You are a true person, loved, experienced in life, positive and tough, so you
will survive this disease. Life has given you abilities that let you heal. Your
immunity will protect you so that it never happens to you again. See it as if
you had a rotten tooth and ate too much chocolate, and the dentist is far
away. We all have to go through it. However, I very much hope to be able to
enjoy your company in the future, and I pray that all the energy that you
have been willing to send to others will now return to you as Good Energy

and protect you. Same Buddha in You. Same Healing Power My Dear !

You have been a relaxed guy since I knew you. I'm telling you about a man who was always tough. Because he had a father who treated him badly when he was young. He made many mistakes and injured people. But he became one of the best karate teachers in the country, simply because out of gratitude that he survived, he wanted to pass it on to as many young people as possible and wants to make them strong. He also teaches you that you don't always have to be hard in life, only then will life teach you what really matters.

People notice by my writing that the external actions of the criminals do not reach me. I know how to use the simple resources offered by nature. We cannot submit to stupidity as easily as they would like. We must not be affected by the corruption of the mediocre. In the same way we must adapt and resist viruses, because the wickedness of men seem to be like a virus that spoils good intentions. Since we have been training for a long time, we will be able to adapt to the circumstances.
Aside from the genital and copulative reductionism that leads to sexuality, I have to say that these days have served to please me lovingly.

We would refrain from drunk Santa Claus.
Would we leave winter to the Russians?
Would we give spring naturellement France.
Would we like the Italian summer ...
and autumn would remain clear to us Germans.

My Sister Carrie, she loves to join in the Women's Sisterhood. And of course we do contact sometimes. This is very very useful ... I know if I try to paint then I don't just paint, because these are paintings that I have seen before in my mind. And if I meet Women then therefore that I have dreamed that I would meet them. And I dream because I have understood things. And of course I do show them who exist in real, because it is better not to fantasize without any backround, but better to understand reality …

I was altime aware that called out numbers that appear right now meant a serious matter, so I denied of being aware of all this, but I took it serious my life through.

If we do think about Christmas and the Nikolaus, we would all start to cry, because there are too many outside who have none that loved them now.
I see everywhere those false Santaclauses telling the wrong things to naivity and helpless searching for help. But the more of them we count the more of Women who suffer pain who ll have to prostitute and do loose their home.
I don't talk about all those kids gettin' game addicted and won't find a way back to school anymore. I talk about them women who just feel on the top of theif lives and get raped even by those they trusted. It's a shame !
Even by their fathers who did it.

Would german woman not always wear men's boots.
Would the lonely guardian of dark thoughts
not always downgrading your own men to idiots.
Would greet all mourners not always remember better times
that have been lost. Would the removal of inanimate youth look confusingly
similar to stupid, faked interests of the disappointed sun-seeker
within rather periodic moon blindness.

I almost felt like I was in the wrong movie !

What part of Germany are you from ?

Babie You can tell that I am part of a Lady. I was born in K-town Americans said so, because in my little town lived 80 000 Americans Soldiers Family and so I can tell, I knew a few of them, we drank some Whiskey together, we went swimming in the nights, we drove to Car Cinemas, we had some drumming in the dark wood, we played bowling in the American center, we went to the Ramstein Airbase Danceball, we danced in our Club, we watched Movies of the „Dune", we had our round about friends thousands everywhere, some took to many drugs and dies, some not.

The 30 000 French Soldiers nobody noticed at all, because we were knowing more French in France than Soldiers .... The house I lived in was directly at the edge of the wood, a taller wood, and nearby a kind of reservate for wild animals, Buffalo, lynx, wild pigs, deer, russian wild horses, and so on. We children found out many things to do there without the grownups day and night... My family from Norwege came everyyears to vistit the grandmother, and she just laughed and said, our family would be so widespread, that she thought it might be, that we do have Hungarians in our family, too, ... what ever who knows ...

OHH Yes We do have some flowers grow in this whole world, growing and telling they would loove to spread in every field, and would spend their time with who ever, but now can't. Who steadily keep in her sleep. Who zoom hereby in her dreams, what could be, but never would be. Then they do have to give more and more top tweets to press all this porno and exhibitionism all around. So those dreams spread in words.

Awesome.

You shouldn't buy from anyone who only sells beds, because it's just the unpaid secretary, who does his business and not her slave driver.
You shouldn't marry women for their looks, because they have so many shoes to fly around the world with, for which there is no closet at all.
You shouldn't buy a nurse's good intentions, because it represents the fool of the nation, she rarely once promoted to the mother of the nation
by a few doctors have no professional life and get married.
You shouldn't just believe a man that he has great knowledge,
as long as he's not proven to have social skills,
because like an old senile professor later,
he needs your help into his cotton pants.

I tell You Carrie, that I do notice just now, written that funny rubbish, that I nearly never slept in real beds since I left my parents house ! Outside on my travels I was a guest, inside and outside. Later I had my first furnitured small room, and left very soon, to an empty house, my first high bed stood there so I used it for a short while through a cold winter without heating. Then I was guest for a while again in different houses on my run away and take off to North. Then I bought something like a sitcouch and used it for sleep for nearly ten years. Then I bought from friends a high bed again, like my son had one. Then we built up a very comfortable new and beautiful high bed for my son, that is my bed from nowadays since he left the house. My dog now has the sitcouch under mine in the sleeping room. But as long as I do remember I did never own one real normal bed as usual people do own ! That is funny that I never realized such a thing until today !

Carrie You have a beautiful family and You are the best Nanny for the grandkids in the world. I am so happy to see, that they are in such a composition all !

That functions like this, telling my neighbours to count on me. Seeing everyone has got a head to thoughts, a mouth to speak, his heart to smile at me, however he used all this, shows all along, makes it how alone he feels.

Outside is a real icy wind, like people leave the others alone and do not think about the consequences, like let them explain the world, but don't act anymore, like a started icy sleep of winter between the people, they chose the wordlessness, the pause between them and spontaneity.
There are still the old who do know about that consequences in their past. Them asking the passers if they do still recognize where they walk where to go and why and if they realize its just icy and old people need a kind of Good Word not to loose their hope that these weathers will change for them waiting for the sun now so long.

But it is never the person coming near or how she looks like.
What matters is her reflection, that might be the same situation that even

110

you might have later on, not suffer and I do know the better you wish all the other ones, the better you get back if you are in need !

It's sunny but cool today here. I went out (with mask and gloves) because Bob doesn't always get some stuff I need, though he tries! Everyone in our community is respecting the rules (including businesses).
And, also, Social -Distancing rules! They are taking it very seriously here !

Ha ! Now try and hide You little Shit !!

Yes this is the challenge to respect the rules. We behave okay here too.
If others buy a lot more in this situation, I beware and keep myself at home and buy less, so that is my plus in my pocketmoney at last. I don't know why there are so many buying in panic so many things ?
This is a bit unlogical. The less order between people, the less discipline, means the more we have to care for what we have, isn't it, and we have to carry each other ?!!

Everyone can make flat jokes.
Towing men in the disco too.
She can crochet, he can fuck, a little too easy,
how the king played father, and the little princess became richer.
Let the prince dance, wait how he knows how to impress.
I prefer the man who feels comfortable under his skin.
Carrying more awareness, contributing fascination yourself.
Who can do what himself no longer needs to play the bitch,
just so as not to annoy the dear girl playing softly,
is more the politically correct variant but has no real character.

I Love You.

One good Day I will solve that problem ...

Man, I ll see.
You just came in the mood to share beautiful minutes, and times after, like having a nice warm meal in the stomache.

I know all those young pretty women they ll never find their Man to love, just in case, they do search for ten twenty years for a speciality their dream in fantasy, and none would fit in, and they would just cook and cook and cook such vegan bullshit more of it, but stay lonely, just in case they would never present their Art of Cooking to make the other happy without themselves. As long as people do just give their action into self satisfying they will have to wait the whole damn life I think so, because none could feed such an Ego !

I see character might come together, and togetherness belongs to each other, so it may please stay together !

Some types of nutrition seem to me to be more decadent, elitist and neo-liberal, in short such people call themselves "alternative", that their children only go to schools in which all children are the same, that is meant, those like them, and none others, from a lower financial class. But the children don't have to know that.

We can dance naked in front of each other.
I could arouse your hunger.
We could wrestle on earth.
I could talk to you for hours.
We could sing karaoke.
I could sit, be silent, meditate with you.
We could practice tango steps.
I could go miles with you.
We could measure our strength.
I could build a bed with you.
We could lick my breasts with cream.

I tried to find a conversation with Frank, but again I found a door slam very close, so I just said it like this : ok then my optimism isn't on the right adress I see. And if he is maybe distracted but just fine, then he tells me better that he is not able to follow me, then I see this might need a few days again or weeks, maybe a half year. Then he can tell me when he's back again to feel positive, I know its not his fault.

Before he ll maybe safe the World and protect Mother Earth. I won't be an idiot anymore. Change the partner could be a good idea !

Stay safe, I am very lucky that You are getting much better. Good News are best for me and of course You !

Redirecting love from man to nation is a nasty trick. Orwell tried to understand this early. If this is true, it stirs up useful emotions, but it fuels a cultural struggle. This means what wants, but condescents have no idea about love !

People only get advertisements for things that are of no use and that no one needs. Everyone uses it. We have already got used to home offices in the past decades of the affluent society. We use glasses that give us the illusion of going to concerts, we fly and race through the air, we run through fictional landscapes without any real adrenaline rush, even without exposing ourselves to any real danger. We love on screen. We order sexual partners home online. We buy with Amazon. We get intoxicated with headphones and drink alone at home. We live alone and under constant sound, without having to be reflected in the other. We have long forgotten to pay attention to our own inner voice. We work from the computer and no longer go outside for a walk. We only spend all the time at home and no longer need to go on vacation. Sport is frowned upon, time is too precious for that.
We do all of this, and we haven't been out the door for a long time.
Only nowadays do everyone have to stay inside for a few weeks and still go crazy ? That's absurd.

No those are the facts and Im not panicking thank you. I face reality.

I don't have to say sorry, my Dear, but imagine that every terrestrial living being has his very own experience with death. I do respect this !
And I too enjoy it peaceful that Your blood is running wild, and your heart opens wide with that protest and You send the fighters energy ... that is that kind of energy that keeps You alive ! It is Your Power to survive, and I am happy about it, that You are definitely in rage each day ! I want to see You fight within the whole next forty years, my Friend !
I was never prouder for a Woman like the One You Are !

I WANT TO PLACE MY SOULS WORDS ALL OVER YOUR BODY SO YOU MAY LIVE IN MY FEELINGS EMBRACE. I AM HEALING EACH DAY AND FEELING STRONGER. YOU SEEM TO BATHE IN ME EXTENDING YOUR WARMTH. WHEN YOU WRITE REMEMBER I HOLD YOUR EVERY BREATH CLOSE...JL

Thanks my Exposure to Death has been extreme sadly ! I have been primary caretaker and then buried my grandparents, parents and all my siblings.

I know and I imagine what that meant maybe to all those liveables on Earth since we are here. There might come really somethings together. I am such a fighter too. And I too had to take this that I am not more special than anybody because of this story. And finally I find the chance to fight for the challenge not to loose my faith in humanity, thank You for that !

You're welcome xxx

I can't wait until this is over so I can return to Hot Yoga !
I have no space here to do it! I am 63 !

Yes. This year I do realize that I finally start to age, but I am 55 that doesn't matter. I too go for jogging outside, and in a few days that winter will leave , and a few pounds that I loose. I am not afraid of the age. I am too conservated with all my experience. I do feel how You feel. Even me it's awful not to move. Then I lie in bed at night and can't breathe. I love more to climb out a bed, okay not have slept, but have relaxed and feel close to the night that gave me safety. But the less I move the older I feel. So I wish You soon a big Change of the situation, Carrie !!

Yes I wish it for you, too.

I ll do something useful, now I ordered an Aloe Healing Plant to my house, because my old lady, she is now more than twenty years old, she won't have the strength anymore to grow and get babies. She is the Aloe Aborescens, grows up like a small tree to 60-70 centimeter, she is not poisoned !
Here a foto - of the new plant:

I had a huge one but Bob left it outside and it froze this Winter.
It was too heavy for me to lift !

I managed to save some of its babies though !

She has the Soul of a Gypsy, the Heart of a Hippy, the Spirit of a Fairy.

I see she comes from Mosambik, Malawi, Südafrika.
Yes, You are right, the yours is sure the type that heals. She looks like mine.
Sure You could use her gallert for wounds, and each skin problem, but I
think she is too worthful to eat her, even she brings power.
I am really happy and look forward to her in 3-4 days !

I see on the pic of Your Plant that she has too these white little stains
on her leaves, and that old Man who sold me mine told me, this is the sign,
that she can be healing ! I wish You a Nice Day Carrie !

You too xxx

I learned to know Robert.
It was yesterday, a gentleman who is a handsome friendly guy from Italy.
I imagined we should have met younger, when I was on travel in his country
with seventeen, maybe in Florence, somewhere in the small streets together
in the sundance or on the beach. Dreams just.

I told him that I miss it to get touched by real love of a man. I feel much
younger with a little sunshine, and like You say, this feelin like Makin' Love
to the one You love, is awake like this prickle in the Air. Like I lay in the
grass yesterday, my dog burrowed in the sand in a deep hole, I had that
feelin like Sun was kissin me, and I knew this heart awakening was
everywhere today like a kid's longing for freedom and jump in the Air !
The kids kind of a Love is different, I see, then this altime owns a special
name and for ever. But my longing to Love is more of a complexer, like
miss his smile, and move and smell. This is not the same innocense like a
child's Love, but it is true too, ... But I see ... my besties always do live so
far away ... and it's me here who wants to embrace all of them !

Handle others anger with a smile.
People are like garbage trucks. Well, they run around with garbage, and
they're full of disappointment, full of frustration, full of anger, and when
their garbage piles up, they need a place to dump it on you, sometimes they
put it on you, but you know what, you don't take it personal, you just wave,
smile and you wish them well, and you move on. Don't let their garbage
spread to the people at work, at home or on the streets. You love those who
treat you right, and you pray for those who don't.

117

See now life is 10 % of what you make it, the other 90 % is how you take it.
This also applies to today's fathers:

Abuse a girl for violence.
Taking the flowers from a girl's hand.
To rape a girl.
It means nothing more than deflowering a girl !

I loved reading the traditional stories . Their irony, the secrets, the
tenderness, the old women who passed on fables to children from all over
the world. As a child, I was not interested in people, their weddings, the
fathers' mistresses or all that unnecessary stuff. Rather, I knew most of what
I could learn from the eyes of the horse, and I perceived the forest as such to
live out all my fantasies in it. How could my son as such not avoid having
this unshakable self-assurance than being the beloved son of his mother ?
If he has become a book lover since ancient times and many torn pages,
I am delighted.

It isn't the mountains ahead to climb that wear you out,
        it's the pebble in your shoe ~ like Muhammad Ali said -
        What I mean by that is that it doesn't matter
        to cause others to believe
        to master what others think
        to heed when others are submissive
        to be sorry if others show weakness and sadness
        it's easy to show everyone first
        what you do, how you do it, and how you feel about it
        coping with what your own life is
        especially with how much humor you are able to carry this burden.

Those who are judged by their "normal behavior" and shouting
"They are normal" generally raise the suspicion that they have a problem.

I have my lust,
the gift comes only from my body.
I set my own goals.
I know how to change,
it's not about me,
to let myself be socially absorbed,
and undergo a partnership by mutual agreement,
just because they asked me to,
so I can sleep better and better,
not to live in fear and insecurity,
to stand in love as abandoned.

In reality, people have not sunk as deep as we fear.
They just never got as high as we thought they were.

120